james **black**

page 3

YOU HAVE BEEN CHOSEN TO **SAVE** THE **PLANET**

There are 100 things in this book
that will make a difference to our world -
some big - some small.

Play your part - pick just **one** of the **100**
and make it your mission to complete ...

Designed by Martha Blades

Edited by Deborah Jean White and Jamie Stangroom

First published in 2022 in the United Kingdom
by Communications TV

Printed and bound in the United Kingdom
on recycled paper

For information address:
james@environment.tv

A catalogue record of this book
is available from the British Library

PRE-RELEASE EDITION (UK)

Paperback ISBN 978-1-7397463-0-8

I dedicate this book to my four children
Alexandra, Lewis, Ben and Victoria.

*Thank you for helping me see
the world as it should be seen.*

A place of adventure and beauty.

ACKNOWLEDGMENTS

I would like to acknowledge the following
wonderful people for their help, advice,
and general pushiness in making this
book turn from a simple idea
to a finished reality:

Deborah Jean White,
Jamie Stangroom, Lily Dawkes,
Kate Long, Peter Knight, Joe Toward
and Julia Black.

Kindness was you shining a torch on my journey,
Wisdom was you carrying spare batteries for the torch.
Thank you.

CONTENTS

YOU HAVE BEEN CHOSEN TO **SAVE** THE **PLANET**

INTRODUCTION

it's not about getting people up the 'green' ladder,
it's about getting people on the ladder in the first place

The premise of this book is very simple. It understands that most of us can see we are facing a climate crisis that may destroy all life on this planet. It acknowledges that most of us actually care about the environment, and it believes that, given a chance, most of us want to do do something positive. It also understands that most environmentalists 'go on a bit' and seldom make helping the Earth seem sexy, fun, or even interesting.

The book then lists 100 things - large and small - that can be done to help reduce, slow, or even reverse climate change.

It then asks the reader to go through the list of 100 and pick just one idea they like - and do it themselves. Just one. Easy.

Readers may already do some of the 100 things mentioned in the book, so there is also a little star everyone can tick to see how well we are all doing. It would be a waste to lose this information, so it would be a nice piece of research if people used the hashtag **#IDoThisAlready** and simply note your figure out of the 100. The average number is just 9 if you want to compare.

The book also throws in a few nice facts along the way to make things relevant and fun, in the hope that people can have a good read and enjoy a smile or an 'oh really' moment.

Finally, this happy little collection of words and ideas hopes to help people see that being 'green' can save us money, make us money, improve our health, help feed us, keep us safer, make our homes more efficient, and give us better and cleaner transport.

Wherever in the world you find yourself reading this book I hope you enjoy the words ahead. If you can, why not take a selfie of where you are and post it to **#ChosenToSaveThePlanet** letting everyone know which task you have chosen.

After all the many months of writing, it would be nice to see where the words on this keyboard finally end up.

James Black
james@environment.tv

Make Reasonable Choices

If you've ever watched the 2010 Hollywood film, *The Other Guys* you will no doubt remember the scene where Samuel L Jackson and Dwayne Johnson, as Detectives Highsmith and Danson, jump from a skyscraper in pursuit of a group of elite professional criminals. Before they jump, Danson says, 'aim for the bushes'. We then see the couple flailing in the air before coming to a very predictable and very nasty death when they slam into the sidewalk below. 'Aim for the bushes' is now a byword for supreme overconfidence and has been the source of countless memes. They managed all this from being in a 1 hour 47 minutes long film for just 6 minutes and 20 seconds.

The actual lead roles in the film were played by Mark Wahlberg and Will Ferrell, but they literally had the film stolen from them by one of the funniest moments in cinema.

Three years later, Will Ferrell managed to 'steal the show' himself, this time in an uncredited cameo role in the Owen Wilson and Vince Vaughan film, *The Internship*, (google it if you don't know what the movie is about!). In the film, at a point where the duo have lost their jobs but have the chance of a new beginning, Wilson's mattress-store owning brother-in-law tries to stop him leaving for California. Played by Ferrell, the brother-in-law points to a large tattoo on his neck and says, 'you know what this says'. Wilson replies 'I don't read Sanskrit', to which Ferrell says: 'make reasonable choices'.

Regardless of anyone's actual view on tattoos, the point was made. The tattoo may advocate for making reasonable choices, but a tattoo on the neck stating that fact, may not have been itself a reasonable choice. Even worse, the tattoo wasn't even in Sanskrit, but Hindi, and was misspelled.

Sometimes what we think, what we say, and what we do can be all at odds.

With regard to the environment, it is better if people make 'reasonable choices' than 'impossible choices'. People want to do the right thing but should not beat themselves up when they don't do the right thing, or feel guilt about having done things in the past, that they now know to be harmful to the planet. In essence, don't get bogged down by firm black and white environment principles, just be smart and use your common sense.

If you can get an electric car, good on you, do it, but if your budget is really tight or you already own a fairly new petrol car, it might make more sense, and be more reasonable, to keep the car you've already got until a later point. If you've had a pet for years, don't feel any guilt about the effects it may be having on the environment. Leave that conversation until a time, hopefully a lot further down the line, when you are considering a new pet.

Yes, be committed to helping the environment personally and inspire those around you to do likewise, but turning overnight into an 'enviro-evangelical' will do no favours. Having a go at people because their homes aren't metre-depth insulated, or arguing with people about their Christmas flight to Lapland, or turning every conversation, whether it be about avocados or zoo animals into a 'debate' about the environment, will only alienate people.

Whatever you personally choose to help the planet, whether it be walking to work, mending clothes, growing food, making things last, recycling, staycationing, or not buying fast fashion - take simple pride in the actions you make. As Mahatma Gandhi, a man who was no stranger to effecting change, once said, 'glory lies in the attempt to reach one's goal and not in reaching it'.

And don't forget, if you are ever on a skyscraper trying to catch a criminal below, make the reasonable choice - use the stairs, or grow bigger bushes!

Impact: Makes small change. Leaves no impact on skyscraper sidewalks.
Difficulty: Change is hard.
Money-saving: Yes.
Action: Simply be the best person you can be regarding the environment.

I Do This Already  **I Choose This Task** ☐

If You Need to Drive, Go Electric and Buy, Beg, Steal* or Borrow to Do So

The world loves driving - a love so strong we collectively own just over 1.5 billion vehicles. Proof of this love is that over half of drivers have nicknamed their cars, while one in five admit to preferring their car to their partner.

The usual measure of the power and prowess of a car is how quickly it can get from a standing start to 60mph (96.56kph). The world's best-selling petrol/diesel car of all time, the Toyota Corolla (over 44 million sold and still counting), can rock a comfortable 8.2 seconds. The 8.0-litre, 16-cylinder Bugatti Chiron (if you need to ask the price you can't afford it**) can do this in 2.4 seconds. Compare these times to the Aspark Owl, which can do exactly the same in 1.7 seconds. Impressive, 'rad', 'lit', I hear you car nuts and speed freaks scream, but what is really awesome is that the fastest one doesn't pollute the planet from the fuel it uses - it's all-electric. This means, one of the fastest cars in the world can be powered by a wind turbine out in the North Sea or a solar panel in the Mojave Desert.

According to the European Parliament, transport accounts for nearly 30 percent of the European Union's CO2 emissions and that is fairly similar in North America. The biggest part of that is made up by road transport at 72%, while the rest comes from water navigation (13.6%), civil aviation (13.4%), railways (0.5%) and 'other' (0.5%).

If people want to help save the planet in a big way then everyone changing their vehicles from petrol/diesel to all-electric cars, trucks, vans and motorcycles, could reduce global carbon emissions by around one-fifth. This one move alone shows how big a difference individuals really can make.

One of the big put-offs to owning an electric car is 'range anxiety', essentially the fear of running out of power far from a charging point. This was maybe a realistic concern when the average range was less than a hundred miles, but as we are now in an era when electric cars such as the Tesla Model S, Hyundai Kona, Jaguar i-PAce, Kia e-Niro, Mercedes-Benz EQC and a host of others can all travel over 250 miles before they need refuelling, and charging points are almost everywhere - that fear is fading away. Even supermarkets have charging points these days.

Electric cars are also not cheap, yet. But they are getting less expensive with every new model produced. On the very big plus side, the cost of refuelling an electric car, dependent on where you live in the world and the price of electricity and petrol/diesel, can be as good as one-fourth of the cost of driving the same make petrol/diesel fuelled car. Fuel price is not the only benefit, most governments, as well as state and city authorities absolutely love electric vehicles. Norway, for example, offered free parking, tax breaks and use of bus lanes to encourage electric car use. Today, Norway is one of the biggest adopters of electric cars - and drivers there are 17 times more likely to drive an electric car as a driver in the USA. Also, many cities are banning, or charging a toll, for cars that are 'fossil fuelled'. London, for example has introduced the Ultra Low Emission Zone (ULEZ) which charges £12.50 a day for most older petrol/diesel cars to use the roads - but is free for electric vehicles.

In short, as soon as you can, drive electric - it's cooler, cheaper, and helps people breathe better - and, unlike that pollution maker you currently drive, you'll have a better chance of being able to resell it in five years time!

*don't actually steal, that's bad.
**the price is around $3 million.

Impact: Could reduce global carbon emissions by up to one-fifth.
Difficulty: Easy but initially expensive.
Money-saving: Yes, over time.
Action: Use electric vehicles where possible.

I Do This Already  **I Choose This Task**

Plant a Tree on Your Birthday

If you ask an environmentalist when is the best time to plant a tree, there is roughly a one in three chance the witty reply will be, 'twenty years ago'. In part, this response is because most environmentalists want to be seen as funny, but also because they understand we really should have been planting millions more trees a long time ago and are now having to play catch-up.

Without sounding too tree huggy, trees are actually pretty cool. They help the environment, and humanity, by drawing in water, plus carbon dioxide from the air, then use the power of the sun to chemically turn this into food so they can grow. The fantastic by-product of this process is oxygen.

This is such a great process, and something society would see as a miracle if it had only just arrived as a new invention:

'the tree - a mostly pretty looking, self sustaining biological machine, that takes nasty climate change making carbon dioxide in at one end and feeds out life giving oxygen at the other'. Brilliant, plus it can be used to store carbon and, at the same time, when finished with, can help you build a house or furniture.

In reality, trees are not the only way of removing carbon dioxide from the atmosphere, indeed some 70% of all oxygen on the planet comes from similar processes with kelp, phytoplankton and other marine plants in the oceans. But, trees are something we know make a big difference, and they are something we as individuals can plant ourselves.

According to the United States Department of Agriculture one large mature tree can provide enough oxygen to enable four people to breathe. Of course, this is a mature tree, not one we just planted, so it might be better to equate one tree per year to the amount of oxygen you personally take out of the planet by breathing - then feed back as carbon dioxide.

Looking at the idea of 'One Tree Equals Me' it is then really simple to repay the Earth by planting one tree per year - and what better time to make this gesture than on your birthday - a date seldom forgotten. If you live long enough, this might create the equivalent of a small forest.

Moving this notion forward, it is also worth giving a tree to someone for their birthday or to celebrate a special occasion. Few people can remember the presents they were sent last year, never mind what the card they received looked like - or even said. Yet, for a similar, or much lesser price they could be given something that is always there as a pleasant reminder, they can watch grow, or even reward them with fruit.

Giving a tree to someone who lives in an apartment, or doesn't have much space, might be difficult. Not surprisingly, numerous charities and environmental groups have come up with solutions to help. Many will plant a tree in someone's honour in various locations around the world. Your birthday can help reforest the Amazon, regreen parts of the Sahara or make our local parks look nicer. And there is enough space - ETH Zurich's Crowther Lab worked out there are 0.9 billion hectares of land on the planet, mostly in Russia, USA, Canada, Brazil and China, suitable for reforestation by 1 trillion trees - enough they estimate to capture two-thirds of human-initiated carbon emissions.

One other great tree event in much of the world is Christmas, which tends to involve chopping trees down to put in our homes for a few days. One green solution to this is to buy, or grow yourself, a Christmas tree in a pot. If watered correctly it should be fine for planting, minus tinsel, in the New Year.

Happy Birthday, Happy Anniversary, Happy Holidays, and welcome to the new tradition of planting a tree to mark this auspicious occasion.

Impact: A birthday tree planted for everyone equals 7.9 billion extra trees each year.
Difficulty: Easy.
Money-saving: Yes-No-Maybe.
Action: Plant a tree on your birthday and/or other celebration.

I Do This Already  **I Choose This Task** ☐

Find a Place for Everything and Keep Everything in its Place

Have you ever held a US $100 dollar bill? If so, you may have noticed the picture on the note of a slightly balding old guy with a mullet hairstyle from an age before mullets officially existed. This gentleman's name is Benjamin Franklin, the Boston-born son of an English farmer who, when he wasn't chasing lightning with a kite, went on to help draft the US Declaration Of Independence and is sometimes referred to as 'The First American'. He is mentioned here because, even though he wasn't the first to coin the phrase, he is commonly, but mistakenly, credited with popularising the saying: 'a place for everything and everything in its place'. An idea that is so good, it is easily worth that $100 bill in its own right and can definitely save $100 for anyone who reads this book and chooses to organise their 'stuff' in this way.

The actual first use of the phrase comes from a small book which sounds more interesting than it ever was in reality. The book was entitled 'The Naughty Girl Won' compiled by the Religious Tract Society in 1799 and was among their 'Pocket Moral Stories'.

Wherever, whenever, and by whoever the saying was first originated doesn't actually matter. All that really counts is that, more than two centuries later, the idea that if we have a place for everything and put everything in its place, we become more functional, is still so very true.

The idea could simply be thought of as proper storage or easy access to things that help your life. If you know you own something but don't know where it is, or you have ever bought a 'thing' only to later discover you own the same 'thing' already then this is a skill you patently need to acquire.

If you want to work out how having a place for everything and putting everything in its place can help save the planet then let's just take one small thing, a smartphone, and look what could happen if that single item had a fixed and safe place in the home (say, a desk top) or while on your person (say, a zipped or buttoned pocket on a jacket).

A survey compiled by UK firm mobiles.co.uk and published in Forbes in 2020 showed that 74% of people in the UK own a smartphone and, on average, each person has already lost or misplaced it two times in their life. These figures, for a country that makes up just 0.87% of the world's population, suggest that, to date, an estimated 98,324,688 phones have been lost in the UK - and end up being replaced well before their time. The places they are mostly lost are in bars/restaurants (24%) on public transport (24%), on a street or park (23%) - at home (17%), plus many other places such as canal lock gates (personal experience!). Each phone replacement is expensive to the individual, but to the planet it is estimated that each new phone needs 10 to 15 kilograms of ore to be dug from the Earth to get the raw materials such as iron, copper, nickel, tin and rare earth metals such as tungsten and cobalt, plus precious metals like gold and silver, all so it can be made again.

If that zipped pocket stopped just ten percent of phones being lost in the UK there may well have been 9.8 million phones continuing their useful life, and 122,000 tonnes of ore safely left where it's been for millennia - in the ground.

The world will buy 1.4 billion new smartphones this year, a figure that could be lowered if we stopped losing them. Keep it, and your other things safe, and exactly where you can find them by doing as Benjamin Franklin would do - 'having a place for everything and putting everything in its place'.

Impact: Reduces extra need for thousands of tonnes of precious metals and other materials.
Difficulty: Easy.
Money-saving: Yes £100+
Action: Give everything you own a fixed, secure, and memorable home.

I Choose This Task ☐

Carry Your Own Bottle or Cup

In a few countries around the world, like Germany, you will often see people wandering the streets clutching an empty plastic bottle. They will walk past trash cans, recycling bins, even roadsweepers with dustcarts, all without handing over their bottle. If you tried to take the bottle from them you would probably end up in a fight.

The reason for this apparently bizarre behaviour is simple, they have purchased a bottle that is 'pfand', meaning it had a deposit paid on it when the drink was originally purchased, and is destined for the 'pfandautomat', the bottle return machine. This hole in a wall contraption, normally located at the front of supermarkets will take the bottle and return you a €0.25 coupon, repayable as cash in store or towards your next shopping bill.

Such a nice system, it turns waste into money and means recycling/reuse rates go through the roof as people refuse to litter their drink bottles because they want the cash. Even if they did litter them on the street, there is an army of mostly pensioner environmentalists who will instantly pick them up for their own shopping money. No massive litter problems in German parks and the country now enjoys recycling levels for glass and plastic bottles as high as 97%. What is trash in one country becomes a recycling dream in another.

Sadly, most of the world has no such system, and every bottle we buy is left to the mercy of its temporary owner. Some get used again, with countries like the UK recycling 59% of their plastic bottles, while the USA has dipped to 27.9%. Where the rest of the 500 billion plastic drinking bottles produced each year go is up for debate, but they are mostly shared by landfill, incineration, or littering our land until they end up in rivers and oceans. No surprise that microplastics are now found in sea salt - and salt is found in most foods.

Naturally, even in places that have great bottle recycling facilities it would make more sense for people to use their own bottle, cup, mug or flask.

In the case of plastic bottles the average person in the USA, as an example, will use 13 bottles a month, or 156 a year. Assuming the drink is just water and the cost per bottle is 60c that means an annual spend of $93.60.

The average cost of a good dishwasher safe reusable water bottle is $7.50 and is expected to last at least two years. The cost of filling the bottle with tap water is less than 1 cent. Adding 156 fill-ups over just one year at $1.56 to the $7.50 cost of the bottle means a spend of just $9.06 - a whopping $84.54 saving over single-use bottles. More importantly, we are not allowing 156 unnecessary plastic bottles to find their way into the environment. The reusable bottle owner, now much less poorer, is not likely to change back to expensive single-use bottles of water - especially as, like most people who move away from single-use bottles, they quickly notice the health benefits as they are more likely to increase their water intake, and are able to manage and measure their hydration more accurately.

If you have the space to do so, carrying your own mug or thermal flask also helps the environment as it removes the need for single-use plastic cups. In some cafes and coffee/tea outlets this may even get you cheaper drinks, as there are often incentives and discounts to customers who bring their own cups.

One particularly nice way of removing/reducing single-use cups is a system traditionally used in various cities, especially in Germany, that have Christmas markets. The price of the mug is added to the drink and the buyer can keep it as a memento or simply hand it back at any time and get their cup money returned. Win-Win.

Impact: Massive reduction in the 500 billion plastic bottles made each year.
Difficulty: Easy.
Money-saving: Yes £50+
Action: Buy own bottle. Use own bottle.

I Do This Already  **I Choose This Task** ☐

Share Old Photographs You Don't Want Rather Than Putting Them in Landfill

Ever heard of Robert Cornelius? No, he isn't a character in 'Planet of the Apes', or a Danish football player, or the guy who invented beer. In reality, he was the person who took the world's first ever selfie - and we know he did because in a world of 'pics or it didn't happen', we still have the image readily available for all to see on the internet - or via special access (it is so fragile) at the US Library of Congress in Washington DC.

The photograph was taken in October 1839 at the back yard of the Cornelius family store in Philadelphia, which is 174 years before the Oxford English Dictionary announced 'selfie' to be their 'word of the year' in 2013.

The reason we mention Cornelius is that he had a working knowledge of metallurgy and chemistry, and understanding metals and chemicals was a vital part of the daguerreotype photographic process used at the time. The process used silver-plated copper and mercury vapour. Modern selfies are sometimes taken in very dangerous places but developing the original selfie was, chemically, a way more hazardous experience.

Today, old photos, and negatives, come from different parts of the history of photography, a history that employed various processes containing an array of chemicals. This makes many difficult to recycle. Most old photos are safe, but a very small number of negatives, such as those using cellulose nitrate used until the 1950s, are considered dangerous. They can become unstable at 38C, catch fire easily, burn extremely quick and hot, and don't need oxygen to burn and produce toxic smoke. No surprise then, they are banned from all public transport in the UK and cannot be shipped by the US Postal Service.

Most people have some old photographs somewhere in their home. Many of long gone relatives, or people we don't know or can't remember, and locations that could be anywhere and seem lost in time. There is always a temptation to simply throw them away as yet more dirty landfill, but, this is an act of social and environmental vandalism. They do still have a great use, they can be given to photo historians who can digitise them, then have them stored or, if not needed, professionally recycled/disposed.

That image you see as trash may be useful to future historians - it may be the photo that could finally resolve a question to which the world has long sought the answer. It could be the only photo in existence of someone's gran, a pre-famous celeb, even of someone's childhood pet or old house.

There are an estimated 1.4 trillion photos taken each year, over 90% on digital cameras, which works out at 128 pictures per person for everyone on the planet. We also live in a world where face recognition and location identification is becoming easier and more accurate every day. It will not be that long before those old images, once saved and digitised, can be scanned and sorted. In time, these images can be compared and the unknown people will get a name and the mystery locations will become located - and all because people chose not to chuck them in landfill.

For those who have already digitised their photographs and are interested in checking if their old physical ones can actually be recycled, here is a fairly useful little guidance rhyme (which gives the answer No, No, Yes):

If it won't tear, don't put it there
If it tears in tiers, then have your fears
If it tears clean and thin, use recycling bin.

Impact: Ensures proper disposal of toxic waste. Socially useful.
Difficulty: Easy.
Money-saving: No.
Action: Sort photo collection. Digitise everything you can and give unwanted photographs to a local library.

I Do This Already ★ **I Choose This Task** ☐

Pack Your Luggage Like a Ninja

There are many among us who just don't travel well. In cars they are the ones with a roof-rack bursting at the seams on top of a vehicle that no longer has windows at the side, or rear, as they have been transformed into picture frames of jumpers, coats, pillows, skis, mattresses, books and beachballs, all squashed against the insides. In hotels and airports, they are the living embodiment of clutter, normally the flustered ones with two large suitcases each, a series of smaller bags, at least one plastic bag, and a look that screams, 'I'm tired, stressed, and should have stayed at home'.

Compare this look to how you envision a ninja. Those 15th century Japanese assassins, mercenaries and spies, so beloved in popular culture today. Traveling with the wind, unseen, focused, and carrying simple black garb and belt, a sword, and the trademark 'tenugui', the multipurpose thin cloth head cover used in martial arts that also acts as a climbing aid or weapon.

It may come as no surprise, but, of the two types of traveller, the one who helps the environment best is the light, agile and unencumbered ninja. That said, with swords, they do get stopped more often at airport security these days.

So, how do we learn to pack our luggage like a ninja, minus the sword, and help save the environment? We start with the most obvious thing, whether the journey is one day, one weekend, one month, or one year - we accept we can always travel using the same small luggage carrier. No more superheavy 70 litre suitcases that we will always fill. Today we use a modern lightweight backpack small enough to sit on your lap on a bus, at your feet in a taxi, on your back while walking or riding, or go as carry-on in a plane. The backpack should be as slim as possible, have many compartments, and be extremely functional and weatherproof regardless of location or climate.

There are hundreds of tips on how to travel light so you can YouTube yourself crazy and pick the ones that suit you best. Among the most sensible ideas are to pack the heaviest stuff at the bottom, fold or roll clothes into little self-contained 'day' packages, take just one pair of jeans, and never carry more than one pair of shoes. A travel tip common to many flight attendants, is to take a wide scarf, sarong or pashmina, as it can be used as headrest, blanket, towel, cover, curtain, wrap, even a makeshift picnic table.

Pack important stuff only - and make a 'vital items only' list before you pack. If it's not an absolute necessity or serious medical requirement, it should never be needlessly lugged around the world.

The big no-no's include too many electronic items (one phone is surely enough), heavy clothes (layers are better), books and toiletries (they will be available wherever you are going), plus ridiculous stuff like big files filled with papers, travellers cheques, jewellery, washing powder, even tins of soup.

There is an environmental purpose to travelling like a ninja. A pair of jeans with a belt, for example, weigh roughly 1kg. Virgin Atlantic state that if all their passengers reduced the weight of their luggage by just one kilogram each they could save 4000 tonnes of CO_2 each year.

There are many benefits of packing like a ninja. If you drive, you can now travel comfortably, less fuel is needed, and you can even put people, instead of luggage, on the seats. You now also have the option of easily using all other forms of transport. If flying, you are now nimble and unflustered, never pay excess baggage, never wait at a baggage carousel, pass seamlessly through airports, stop-off anywhere, never need to tip a porter, have what you need with you, and packing and unpacking is a breeze.

Impact: Reduces CO_2 emissions, the main initiator of climate change.
Difficulty: Hard initially, but easily learned.
Money-saving: Yes £100+
Action: Watch videos, read lessons, on how to pack efficiently.

I Do This Already  **I Choose This Task** ☐

Treat Yourself to an Electricity Free Hour Each Week

If you are young or not absolutely sports mad, you may have never heard the name Chris Waddle, but this very likeable gentleman was once the third most expensive football player in the world. He is mentioned here because he is also a truly iconic figure, likely never to be forgotten, in the world of electricity generation.

Way back on 4th July 1990 the world was coming to the latter stage of an event that comes around for just one month in every four years, is watched globally by 3.5 billion people, just less than half the world's population, and literally shadows out everything else that is normally considered news.

The England football team had got themselves through the early stages and were now, after almost a quarter of a century, in the semi-finals of the FIFA World Cup. The game was being played at Turin's 'Stadium of the Alps' in Italy against their old footballing enemy, Germany. The winner would go on to Italy's capital, Rome, to play in the final against Argentina - a country the UK had been at war with just a few years earlier. The scene was set, and by anyone's measure this was a very big game but, even so, it ended 1-1 after extra time and would ultimately be decided by penalties. Back home, the country held their breath as the final penalty for England was taken by Chris Waddle. Sadly, his shot flew over the net. England were out, and it seemed the whole nation did what most Brits do in a situation like this - they got up and made a cup of tea. In an instant, kettles, cookers, lights, and fridges were clicked into action. Chris Waddle's missed kick had just created the biggest surge event in UK electricity history.

Every country has energy spikes. In the US, for example, these are regular during Super Bowl ads. Energy demand always fluctuates on a minute to minute basis. In most countries, winter generally has higher demand than summer, daytime higher than night, and midweek higher than weekend. On a typical weekday in a country with defined seasons, energy demand picks up at 6am, grows to 9am as everyone gets ready for work, stabilises until around 4pm when, for the next three to four hours, demand goes up again as people get home, turning lights on, making food, and generally being active. Demand then tails off until midnight then stays constant overnight. In summer, the evening surge disappears as days are longer and warmer.

Using this info we can help the environment. We can simply take a short period, preferably when electricity demand is high, and we just 'switch off' - just for one hour, each week on a day and time of our choice.

In winter, optimum hours to choose would be midweek 5pm to 8pm, while in summer these would be midweek 11am to 1pm, or 4pm to 6pm.

A relaxing once a week candlelit chat with a glass of wine in the winter, or a summer day sat in the garden or park with a good book. Whatever you choose, it it can be part paid for by the 0.5% reduction in your electricity bill!

Obviously, don't turn off vital things, like fridges, keep it regular, and try not to do the same hour as others - or start and end exactly on the hour mark. All you are doing is picking one hour of the 168 hours in the week to reduce your energy needs. If we all did this then the world could reduce its energy output by half a percent.

To help find the other half percent then do a regular 'film night'. Watch a film at home, turn all lights and unnecessary electricity off, watch the film in the dark, cinema style, and save two hours of otherwise wasted energy.

Impact: Possible to remove generation of over 0.5% of electricity.
Difficulty: Easy, and fun.
Money-saving: Yes £5+
Action: Pick regular time to unplug from electricity for one hour.

I Choose This Task

Use Wooden Hangers and Micro-Change the Planet

The idea for this book came about because, even though we can all see we are under real threat of witnessing the destruction of the only planet in the universe on which we know there is life, many of us are just sitting back, ignoring, putting hope in others, or simply accepting our calamitous fate.

Most of us feel so completely powerless to change things. In fact, this helplessness and feeling of paralysis, even has its own medical term, 'climate change anxiety', also known as 'eco-anxiety'.

We want to do something, we need to do something, but we don't actually know what we can do to change things.

The idea then formulated that there must be thousands, indeed millions, of things we could do to turn things around. Some big, like using only renewable energy, some sensible, like planting trees, and some small, like picking up litter.

Then there are the micro-changes, the things so small, we can't directly see how they can make a difference, but when added together can make for supersized change.

One of those things, so trivial, is how people hang their clothes. In fact, a conversation about how things as simple as wooden clothes hangers can help save the planet, was one of the first ideas of some simple changes people could do to reduce climate change.

So, for real, we put forward that your choice of clothes hanger can play a role, however minute, in whether our planet becomes the Eden we all want it to be or the barren wasteland the predictions suggest is coming our way.

The clothes hanger was patented on 12th January 1869 when a Mr O A North of New Britain, Connecticut, was granted patent US85756A for his 'Improvement in Clothes Hook'. Today, there are literally dozens of varying designs, and those made from thin metal wire and/or various different plastics are sold at a rate of 900 million items a month.

Fast fashion accounts for the majority of hangers (think supermarket shirts) and most never see a real wardrobe. Less than 20% are reused or recycled and some 5 to 8 billion a year end up in landfill where they can leach styrene, toluene, benzene, bisphenol and other chemicals into the ground.

The big question, of course, is do you even need them? Could you remove 50% of your clothes and not notice the difference? And, of what's left, how many of those clothes actually need to be hung up? If you could save half the space in two wardrobes that you already use, could you then gift, sell, or donate the unused wardrobe? If so, you've just saved the average £525 price of ever having to buy its replacement. This also means a 50% reduction in clothing replacement, which, if we all did it, would mean that 450 million new hangers a month would need never be made. It would also mean 50,000 of the things packed into each standard 20ft container would not need the 108,000 trucks to move one year's worth across the globe.

If you do need hangers, choose good quality wooden ones for the clothes that are special to you and need to keep their shape. Wood not only stores CO2, but if you use a cedar wood hanger they have a natural odour that repels moths and other insects. Moth-eaten clothes may seem trivial but, as the average American buys 65 items of clothing a year, replacing just 1% of that would mean having to produce, again, another 216 million items.

Impact: Saves up to 108,000 truck journeys worth of exhaust fumes.
Difficulty: Easy.
Money-saving: Yes £100+
Action: Use own wooden hangers and never accept store ones.

I Do This Already  **I Choose This Task** ☐

Only Flush the 3 P's - Poo, Pee and Paper

In 2017, the world's attention was drawn to Whitechapel in London, where a blockage had been discovered in the sewer system that, at 250 metres, was longer than four Leaning Towers Of Pisa on their side. This impassible 130 tonne hardened mass was mostly made up from congealed fats, wet wipes, grease, oil, sanitary products, condoms, and cotton wool, plus many other nasties you should never have to imagine. The fatberg, as we all discovered these things were called, quickly acquired the nickname 'Fatty McFatberg'.

The 'lucky' sewerage experts tasked to remove the blockage worked day and night, but their efforts to sort the mess still took nine weeks and cost over £1 million. This affected hundreds of homes and businesses in the area, and sections were later exhibited, carefully, at the Museum of London.

The 'fatberg', a thing which had only been in our dictionaries since 2008, had hit the world stage. It was not the first, but it was a biggie, and is now something happening regularly in other cities and towns around the globe.

The reason for the fatberg, indeed the reason for the majority of sewer blockages, is simple - we put things down toilets we shouldn't, at the same time as our kitchen sinks churn extra fats into the sewer system from our much changed diets compared to 100 years ago.

Fatbergs may be amusing, but if your home or garden is among the one in 445 affected each year by a sewer blockage, it is difficult to smile as you watch, and smell, a toilet backing up with gifts you thought had long gone.

More importantly, most of what the world puts down toilets, baths, sinks and showers will eventually end up in our rivers and oceans. And the United Nations state only 31% of the globe has access to sanitation services where wastewater is treated.

The solution to this totally unnecessary environmental problem is to use your toilet for just three things - the 3 P's - Poo, Pee and Paper.

Other than to not forget the final 'P' stands for just 'toilet' paper (not newspaper, A4 paper, wallpaper, flypaper, litmus paper, graph paper, grease paper, carbon paper, cardboard, books or kitchen roll), it's that simple. Of course, if you can't remember the third 'P' and live in an area with plentiful water, then it might be better to use a bidet. After all, each year, the adult human flushes around 145 kilograms (think 7 large suitcases) of poo down the toilet, something we need to definitely keep flowing.

As for the 'fat' in the fatberg, there are two very useful methods of reducing this part of the problem before it even starts. The first comes from changing our diets to less fatty options, the second from collecting any fats separately that accumulate in the cooking process.

In countries such as Spain, Belgium and Austria, there is often a small container near the kitchen sink for used cooking oils. These are then collected at recycling points and filtered to create energy as biodiesel fuel, animal feed, even detergents. Other countries suggest you include used fats and cooking oils alongside plate scrapings in your local food waste recycling.

Crazy as it sounds a simple kitchen strainer (cost 50p) could also help save the environment and millions of pounds in unnecessary work. Strainers stop bigger items going down the sink and into the sewers where they tangle with other bigger items and eventually completely block the pipes.

Simple stuff, but considering blocked sewers are normally only noticed when they cause waste to flood or 'back-up' into areas we don't want it, like clean water supplies, homes, offices, schools, etc., it's quite an important step.

Impact: Saves 145 kg of your personal waste floating back into your home.
Difficulty: Easy.
Money-saving: Yes-Maybe £100+
Action: Use strainer in sink. Stick to the 3 P's down the toilet - Poo, Pee and Paper.

I Do This Already  **I Choose This Task** ☐

GPS Your Route Save Fuel and Reduce In-Car Arguments

Way back in 2008, a group of bird watchers were visiting Gibraltar Point, a national nature reserve along the coast of Lincolnshire in England, when they witnessed something they rarely viewed through their binoculars. Along the narrow access road was a large truck - some 2722 miles (4381km) away from its home in Antakya, Turkey. The driver, Necdet Bakimci, was not only stuck, he was also 1001 miles (1611km) away from his actual destination, the British Territory of Gibraltar at the mouth of the Mediterranean. He had mistakenly entered the wrong 'Gibraltar' on his GPS satellite navigation system and been trusting enough to follow it all the way.

This amusing error soon became global news and was used as a launch pad to discuss how GPS systems were mistakenly sending us all over the place. Examples came of drivers in Utah almost going over cliffs, cars being driven onto beaches in Australia, even a limo driver in Salzburg, Austria, attempting to drive down a flight of steps.

The same year a much less publicised report noted that, when used properly, GPS satellite navigation could save 'up to' 16% in fuel consumption. Indeed, a TV motoring show in the UK did a piece on using the 'fastest route' versus 'eco route' options on a 'SatNav' and found, though generally slower, it was possible to save up to 33% in fuel costs using the Eco route

Today, GPS navigation systems are the norm and, while mistakes still happen, like people still pressing 'Lille' in Belgium (small village) when they really want 'Lille' in France (actual city), most people understand exactly how to operate their navigation systems.

Every journey is different and, even for short distances in areas people know well, most drivers have their own preferred routes - which may vary so much they can add over 10% extra fuel or time to the journey.

For those who care about the environment it is possible to easily save a minimum of 5% (likely much higher) in fuel wastage just by using a GPS satellite navigation system to its full potential. Modern systems can work out things like gradients on the journey, number of traffic lights, roundabouts, stop and go areas, speed limits, etc, and combine these with up to the minute traffic flow information to offer you the best 'Eco' route.

If everyone on the planet kept driving exactly as they do now, with the one exception being they used a GPS Sat Nav system, and used it at its most efficient use, then the planet would see a minimum of 5% up to 33% less CO2 emissions from road vehicles.

To put this in context, if we take the European Union, as transport is responsible for almost 30% of the EU's total CO2 emissions, and road transport takes up 72% of that total, this means we could reduce total emissions by around 1.08%, just through properly using GPS Sat Nav.

A recent survey by a UK caravan and motorhome insurance company found just one in ten drivers over the age of 45 always used their GPS Sat Nav, a figure that was one in four for those who were aged 18 to 24. If that figure was 100% then we could make quite a dent in global car exhaust emissions.

One final point worth noting, the number of divorces initiated by map reading incidents during journeys may have reduced, but the number of people who have admitted to instead arguing with their Sat Nav about how bad its directions were was over one in five drivers.

Impact: Over 5% less CO2 emissions from road vehicles.
Difficulty: Easy.
Money-saving: Yes £50+
Action: Use SatNav on majority of journeys - and ALL long journeys.

I Choose This Task ☐

What the Furoshiki is That? Make Your Gifts Mean More

It is estimated that during the Christmas period an extra 30% in waste is generated in Western nations. Much comes in the form of excess food, drinks bottles, old Christmas decorations, Christmas trees, and oversized or unneeded packaging. Saddest of all, however, are the the final two wastes from this time of year - unwanted presents (equivalent to $1 per person), and used wrapping paper (equating to two 5m rolls per person).

Christmas is the biggie on the global gift front, but there are many other gift giving occasions, such as Diwali, Chinese New Year, Eid, Hanukkah, plus Valentine's Day, Halloween, St Nicholas Day, Easter, Mothers Day, Fathers Day, and a host of others, including St George's Day. This final one is not a gift giving day in England, Georgia or Ethiopia, where he is patron saint, but is one of the cutest present days on the calendar in Barcelona, where people give books or roses to good friends and people they love.

Add to this birthdays, of which there are some 21.5 million each day, and not only is that a lot of candles, but a crazy amount of gift wrap.

With regard to unwanted presents, the notion of brand new gifts with a value of a third of a billion dollars in the USA alone going straight to the dump seems wrong beyond belief. From an environmental perspective the answer is to re-use, rather than landfill or recycle. Re-gifting to a person more appropriate for the unwanted present is the logical thing to do, followed by giving to charity or simply selling. If the present is from someone close, it may be better to give it back for them to return to the store and share the money on something nice that you can both share. Win-win is better than bin-bin.

If gifts are being immediately dumped, then the gift itself may be the problem. Perhaps we are giving, or have already received, too much 'stuff' - momentary nothing gifts that no one wants or will remember. Tips from professional gift buyers (yes, they exist!) include: do research on the giftee, give gifts that are relevant and/or fit in with their life, and give gifts that are experiences or offer real practical bonus to their life.

As for the used wrapping, the two 5m long rolls of unrecyclable paper per person landfilled just after Christmas, is equal to everyone, all 7.9 billion of us on the planet, wrapping every inch of Austria - a whole country!

Austria's favourite son, Arnold Schwarzenegger, might not appreciate that or it's 'I'll be back' next Christmas vibe.

The most obvious solution to the wrapping paper problem is to not buy gifts at all (humbug!), give digital gifts, re-use old wrapping paper, or best of all learn the Japanese art of Furoshiki - and anything that sounds like it could be a secret swear word is always a winner.

Furoshiki, which means 'wrapping cloth' but literally translates in English to 'bath spread' is a traditional form of wrapping using beautiful square cloths and folding things inside them so no string or tape needs to be used. It dates back to the 14th century and is so sensible for the 21st century environmental issues we have today, it deserves to make a very disruptive return as the main type of modern gift wrapping.

Gifts seem a little more special when received in a neatly folded cotton furoshiki, and the beauty is that the present is easy to open and the wrapping neatly folded. Even more beautiful is the wrapping can be used time after time as it is passed on between friends and family.

Impact: Stops the unnecessary waste of wrapping the equivalent of Austria every year.
Difficulty: Easy, and very trendy.
Money-saving: Yes, over time.
Action: Give more relevant gifts. Replace wrapping paper with furoshiki wrap.

I Choose This Task

Use Energy Rating Systems When Buying Electrical Products

The average healthy adult can create around 100 Watts of electricity when cycling at a good speed. This is the same power as it takes to run an old 100 Watt lightbulb (or just over five modern 1300 lumen LED bulbs).

If we hooked up every single person on the planet to an electricity generating bike and then asked them to pedal for one hour every day, with only weekends off, then all 7.9 billion of us, young and old, cycling like crazy, would likely create around 50 Watts of energy each. Collectively, after one year, all of humanity, would have created 103 billion kWh of energy - which equates to the same amount it takes to run the whole of the internet.

Incredibly, that 103 billion kWh of human made energy would still be less than half the amount of energy saved each year by consumers who used the ENERGY STAR ratings system in the USA as a guide when purchasing their electrical products - a figure the US Environmental Protection Agency (EPA) states was 230 billion kWh in 2019.

For those interested in saving their money as well as their planet, that meant also avoiding $410 million in energy costs - and the planet missed out on an unnecessary extra 4 million metric tonnes of greenhouse gas in our atmosphere. Other countries use similar energy efficiency ratings systems such as the 'Energy Rating' system in Australia and New Zealand and the European Union 'Energy Label' system.

Energy ratings can help you easily work out how energy efficient a product is so it can be immediately, and accurately, compared with other models. It may seem small, but using the system when purchasing an electrical product is one very easy way of helping relieve the climate crisis - and saving cash.

If we look at the practical use of energy ratings systems then good examples can be found everywhere. A Fridge Freezer may, on purchase price alone, appear 20% cheaper than another seemingly similar item, but when it's running costs are calculated based on its efficiency in comparison to the price of electricity, it may end up actually being 20% more expensive over a period of four or five years.

In places with ever rising electricity costs, by use of simple number crunching alone, it is sometimes more advantageous to buy a brand new A-rated item (the most efficient and the one that uses least energy) than it is to keep your old G-rated item (the least efficient and one that uses most electricity). The savings in electricity alone over a short period will more than make up for the purchase price of a new, less polluting, electrical item. It is worth mentioning, however, that from an environmental perspective, waiting until you have a genuine need for a replacement item is something equally worth considering.

Currently, as an example, on sale in shops, bazaars, large electrical outlets and online stores around the world, the sales people of the planet are merrily selling around $7 billion of dishwashers each year. The more efficient of these dishwashers use an average of 208 kWh in electricity over the year. The least efficient use 462 kWh. Using the European label system as an example, this means for every $100 dollars you would spend on electricity on one with an A-rated Label, you would spend $222.11 on a G-rated one - and that's every year!

Wherever you live, get to understand the energy rating system for electrical products. It is in your financial interest and interests of the planet that you have the knowledge to choose your products wisely.

Impact: Reduce up to half the energy needed for electrical appliances.
Difficulty: Easy, if you have the money.
Money-saving: Yes, over time.
Action: When time comes to renew any electricals go for the best rated items.

I Choose This Task

Be a Little Forker! Use Small Plates and Cutlery

Two common snippets of advice given to those diagnosed as having Type 2 Diabetes are to never eat anything in one session that wouldn't fit in the palm of your hand and to use a small fork when eating your meals. There is some logic in both if you need to eat healthily, but the same advice applies equally to those who want to help the environment.

The idea of not eating large meals is that, for the individual, this reduces the chance of obesity and the many ailments associated with being overweight.

The idea with the small fork, small plate, and/or small spoon, is that, for the individual, it encourages slower, more thoughtful, and ultimately reduced eating. No swooshing down your food in five seconds flat without realising that you've even eaten. Small fork, small plate, is about concentration on your food, making the experience longer and active enjoyment of what you are actually consuming. It is also suggested that people also try 'mindful eating', something practiced by Buddhist monks, which involves eating in silence.

For the environment, if everyone ate just ten percent less then we would need ten percent less resources and, more importantly, ten percent less land to grow it. Food production is estimated to cover 40% of the land surface of the Earth so reducing that by one-tenth would leave 4% of our land free, or 5.96 million square kilometres (2.30 million square miles) available for things that could reduce climate change - like returning lost forests. This would be the equivalent of freeing up a space as big as India and Argentina combined. An added bonus is 10% less fish would be taken from the ocean - and ten percent less fishing could seriously help fish numbers to improve.

The food we eat, and the way in which we eat that food is important for our health and for the environment.

According to the World Health Organization (WHO) obesity has almost tripled around the world since 1975. Among adults aged 18 and over, some 39%, or almost two in every five of us, are overweight, and 13%, or almost one in every seven, are obese. One in seven - that is frightening!

Two other super interesting facts are contained in the World Health Organization data. The first, and possibly one of the best contenders for 'fact of the year', if such a thing ever existed, is that most of the population of the world live in countries where you are more likely to die from eating too much food rather than die from not eating enough. The second fact, and the one that absolutely everyone on the planet should understand, is that obesity is completely preventable.

The suggestion that we have zero need to overindulge is a tale not just of personal medical health - it crosses over into the story of our environment and our overconsumption of its once plentiful resources.

The United States, as an example, has a recorded obesity rate of 42.4% of its adult population according to the CDC (Centers for Disease Control and Prevention). The effects of this on Americans are that diseases including heart disease, strokes, type 2 diabetes and certain types of cancer are on the increase. It also works out for the 42.4% of adults, that their annual medical costs, compared to those Americans who had a healthier weight, were $1429 higher - each year.

The cost of a small fork (actually a pack of four) is around 357 times less than that extra $1429 a year on medical costs.

Impact: Reduces pressure on farm land equivalent to the whole of India and Argentina combined.
Difficulty: Really hard for some, but worth it.
Money-saving: Yes £100+
Action: Use small cutlery. Take time eating. Try not to eat large portions.

I Choose This Task

Junk Mail is 41% Landfill
One Spam Equals One Gram (CO2)

There is something a little unsettling about a person collecting their mail to find yet another unimportant and unsolicited marketing letter addressed to their deceased husband, wife, partner, parent, son or daughter.

Yes, thank you for pre-approving them for your credit card. But they are dead - and you just went to a lot of effort to remind the person left behind of that fact.

Direct marketing, which most people refer to as 'junk mail' can occasionally be useful when used appropriately and in a precisely targeted manner, but is a blight when used wrongly and in a scattergun approach.

Online spam is also intrusive. Thankfully, much is already automatically filtered before it gets to us, but so many organisations we already trust still regularly hit on their 'family' of customers to squeeze a bit more money from our accounts and subscriptions with them. Even notifications on phones are often used by organisations as a sales tool and not just for actual, quite important, 'notifications'.

One common factor shared by the junk mail landing in people's homes and the spam landing on their computers and phones is that both use up valuable resources that the Earth can't really afford to waste.

Junk mail is estimated to make up at least a third of the post delivered to homes across the planet. In the USA, some 129.2 billion items of post are sent each year, while in the UK the figure amounts to 10.2 billion items. If a minimum of 33% of this is junk, and an estimated 41% of that goes straight to landfill unopened, you can see the size of the problem.

There are some very easy things you can do to stop or reduce the amount of junk mail. Most countries have systems that allow householders to opt out of any direct mailing lists. In the USA you can contact DMA Choice, while in the UK there's the Mailing Preference Service. There are 2.3 billion households on the planet and almost all receive junk mail. If every household on Earth stopped just one item of junk mail a week that would mean 119.6 billion letters need never be sent. This is the equivalent of not chopping down every tree in Yosemite National Park every year.

Globally, the number of spam emails sent every single day is estimated to be 249.95 billion. This is over five times as many as the number of legitimate emails. Which is 46.86 billion. Those billions of emails sent, viewed and stored, take up energy. The energy needed to send just one email is estimated to be the equivalent of 1g of carbon, which means all those spam emails sent around the world add up to 249,950 tonnes of CO2 - each day.

The simplest way to reduce spam is to keep your email address as private as possible. Use spam filters. Mark emails that are spam as spam, and delete anything that looks like spam. If it's a real problem you could go nuclear and change your e-mail address. It is also worthwhile unsubscribing or limiting the type of messages sent by trusted sources - a ticked box on their website or app settings should end promo messages, notifications and texts.

Most people don't realise they themselves are innocent spammers - by overwriting (think confirming email of the confirmation of the confirmation of a meeting) - or oversharing (think funny picture sent to all your colleagues). Finally, it is worth remembering two things - replying to spam and junk mail will only ever bring more and, in CO2 terms, one spam equals one gram!

Impact: Save the equivalent of Yosemite National Park in trees each year.
Difficulty: Easy.
Money-saving: Yes £5+
Action: Opt out of direct mail and stop ticking email preference ok boxes.

I Do This Already  **I Choose This Task** ☐

Help Green Brands and Initiatives But Beware of Greenwashing

One of the beautiful things about fruit and vegetables is they come in their own natural packaging. Their skin. This packaging is normally quite durable and can be easily cleaned. It is also totally compostable. Even so, most supermarkets around the world still throw fruit and vegetables in plastic bags or put oversized price stickers directly on their produce.

There are numerous solutions the supermarkets could employ to reduce or even eradicate this problem. The easiest being to have sales staff who know the different fruits and vegetables so little needs to be packaged. They could even laser label all the barcode info needed directly onto the skin of the fruit or vegetable - which works for most produce and is 100 times less carbon emissiony* than it is to glue on a piece of inked paper.

But why would supermarkets, or for that matter companies, brands, organisations, even government, do any of these type of things if they didn't need to, or were not being forced to make a change?

It is at this point that the consumer/user/individual can play a big role. We need to give them a compelling reason. Let them know their positive change for the environment is a thing we like. If you shop at a supermarket and it does something you see as good for the environment (like laser label their melons or avocados instead of using labels and packaging) then we should help their change become a success by buying that particular fruit.

All organisations love to be loved. If they can feel your love (and subsequent increase in profits/kudos/votes/publicity) they won't stop aiming to keep your attention by doing even more of the things they know you like.

Organisations that are genuinely trying to do something positive for the environment need our help to thrive. That small charity working to remove plastics from our rivers needs benefactors, the company installing geothermal heating for homes needs clients, and the coffee chain who sell only 'shade grown coffee' and 100% environmentally friendly cakes needs customers. If something positive is happening, we need to give it fuel to grow. It wasn't that long ago that green ideas like printer ink refills, electric cars, even recycling centres, were the domain of 'hippies' and 'treehuggers' - now they are super normal.

Sadly, it has to be noted that not everything put forward by organisations as being good for the environment is actually good, or real, or accurate, or honest. The problem with 'greenwashing' as it has been labelled, is that it misleadingly leans on our desire to be greener and ends up eroding our trust in many green initiatives.

The term greenwashing first came about in 1986 in an essay by environment campaigner Jay Westervelt, and centered on how some hotel chains were placing signs in guest bathrooms asking visitors to 'save the environment' by reusing towels. In itself this is a great idea, but this concern for the environment did not extend to other areas of the hotel and was merely used to reduce laundry costs and improve profits. Be wary, a product stating it is '50% more recyclable' may be technically accurate and sound like a big deal but means very little if it started at 2% recyclable and went to just 3%. Similarly, the use of terms like 'wholesome', 'green', and 'natural', may suggest things are good - but, technically, uranium, mercury and arsenic (all poisonous) are also 'natural'. Be helpful yes, but never be 'green dumb'.

*'emissiony' is now a word

Impact: Greening of organisations is a top five climate change priority.
Difficulty: Moderately easy.
Money-saving: Not normally.
Action: Encourage organisations by using their green initiatives.

I Do This Already ★ **I Choose This Task** ☐

Don't Get a New Cat, Dog, or other Pet Unless it is Vital to Your Wellbeing

This may come as a surprise but, in terms of sheer numbers (140 million), a whole nation of goldfish and other freshwater fish going by names such as Bob, Bubbles, Goldy, Jaffa, Nemo, Jaws, Captain Jack, Sushi, Long John Silver, Bubba, and Fin are collectively the most common pets in the USA.

In terms of households with pets, those fish, however, are only found in 12 million US homes, while dogs are kept in 64 million homes, cats in 43 million homes and birds in 6 million. All other pets, from reptiles to rabbits to rats, are found in less than 5 million homes each.

Globally, the most common animal found in a home is a dog. Roughly one in 3 homes has a dog. One in 4 has a cat. One in 8 has fish. One in 17 has a bird, and one in 16 has something else like a rabbit, hamster, snake, etc..

The world loves pets, and with good reason. The CDC (Centers for Disease Control and Prevention) in the USA notes that various studies have shown the relationship between people and their pets has many positive health attributes. These include an increase in fitness levels. Decrease in blood pressure and cholesterol, and reduction in feelings of loneliness.

Most dog owners will confirm their pets make them happy. Keep them fit. Introduce them to new people. Make them feel safe. Give their kids responsibility. Even reduce the risks of mental illness.

All good. However the CDC also note that pets can carry zoonotic diseases. This means it is possible humans can become ill from being in their proximity.

For humans, pets are mostly good with a bit of bad. For the environment, keeping pets leans more towards disaster, with a bit of good.

The environment is deeply affected by pets, but not in the way most people assume. For example, in the USA alone, an estimated minimum of 1.3 billion birds and 6.2 billion mammals are killed each year by domestic cats. That's almost the same number as humans on the planet. Even so, bird groups like the UK's RSPB (Royal Society for the Protection of Birds) suggest there is no clear evidence this is the reason bird numbers are actually reducing. They note that even though 100 million animals are killed by cats each year in the UK, a quarter of which are birds, many are weak and sickly. Bird species under the greatest threat, such as tree sparrows, skylarks and corn buntings, seldom interact with cats - and their numbers are reducing for other reasons, mostly change of habitat on farmland.

It is the change in farmland, or more often the need for extra land and resources around the world, that is the bigger issue - and that change is partly brought on by 6% per year increased demand for things like pet food and pet products - a market which is expected to be worth around $320 billion by 2025. When over one third of households on the planet have pets, and those pets no longer eat scraps - that food has to come from somewhere.

The message here is to try not to have unnecessary, or excess pets. You may always have had a dog or a cat, or a rat, or a parrot, snake, budgie, even goldfish - but do you really need a replacement when they have gone?

The cost to the environment of keeping pets is high - and the financial cost to the owners is also significant. In the USA, dogs cost an average of $500 to buy and $1400 per year to keep - a whopping $1900.

If owning a pet enhances your world, then all is good. That said, if you have the chance to be pet-free, or a pet sharer, it is something worth considering.

Impact: Reduces need for increased agricultural land.
Difficulty: Hard.
Money-saving: Yes, £500+
Action: Try not to initiate owning a pet, extra pet, or replacement pet.

I Choose This Task

Be Like the SAS Go Places But Never Leave a Trace

Not too many people, even gung-ho boo-yah military types, have heard of Operation Nimrod. But in May 1980, on Day Six of the Iranian Embassy Siege in London, it introduced the world to a group of people almost nobody had ever heard of before - the Special Air Service - better known as the SAS. And what a spectacular entrance! Elite soldiers, appearing from nowhere. Scaling down buildings. Blowing up walls, windows and doors, from every direction, to access the Embassy after a hostage had been killed. Like a scene from a blockbuster movie they saved the day and the hostages - while leaving the hostage-takers, except one, all dead.

In a few short minutes they had appeared, done their job, then disappeared again. All they left behind was their motto: 'Who Dares Wins'. In an instant, the publicity shy unit became the biggest news story on the planet.

The SAS have since become pretty cool in the eyes of the public, the media, and Hollywood, but most people still don't realise that most of what they do in reality is exactly the opposite of that image. Yes, they train, train, train and train. Yes they are tough. Yes they are determined. Mostly, however, they are stealthy and patient. They can travel thousands of miles, live on the simplest of rations, stay hidden in one spot for days on end, just to observe. Since their formation in July 1941, the SAS may, or may not, have operated in most other countries of the world at one time or another. We'll never know, because on most missions they do something we should all try to do - leave zero trace of ever having been places. On special missions they even carry home their own toilet waste! These guys truly have their sh!t together.

You don't have to be in the SAS, Navy SEALs, Delta Force, Israel's Sayeret Matkal or the Filipino LRR to learn how to leave no trace. But it is worth mentioning these military units because they know even the smallest of things left behind somewhere can end up having dire consequences. It's exactly the same with the environment. What we leave behind will almost certainly cause a problem down the line.

Some cultures already lead the way in leaving no trace. Visitors and viewers watching the 2018 FIFA World Cup in Russia were amazed when, having just won their game against Columbia, the Japan fans cheered like crazy - then spotlessly cleaned up their section of the stadium before leaving. The idea of littering just isn't normal in their national psyche - it upsets the balance. Senegal fans, also respectful, similarly gave the world a show of cleaning up after themselves.

Japan and Senegal Fans 1 - Rest of the World 0.

Wherever you go, leave no reminder of your presence. Whether you have a drinks cup at the Bears Stadium or you are the proverbial bear in the forest!

What do bears do in the forest? Well, if you need to do the same, there is actually a proper etiquette for relieving yourself. If you need to do a number one, go away from the paths and try to pee on trees or rocks rather than plants (most urine doesn't affect plants but it may be an attractant for wildlife who may squash or dig around plants). If it's a number two, go further away from the path, dig a small hole then put the clump of soil, turf or whatever back over the hole when you've finished. You can even put toilet paper in the hole as long as it is unbleached, uncoloured and unperfumed. Anything else - go SAS - and carry it home.

You were here - yes - but no one should ever know.

Impact: None - zero - and that's the point.
Difficulty: Easy for the prepared.
Money-saving: Yes. You will never be fined for littering.
Action: Always be prepared. Take your own mess home and recycle/bin properly.

I Do This Already  **I Choose This Task** ☐

Buy Local Plants Not Flying Flowers And No Need For Air Fresheners

The largest building in the European Union in terms of the amount of land that the structure covers - its footprint - is found in the Netherlands. It is a similar size building to the Tesla Factory in Fremont California or the Jaguar Land Rover plant in the UK. This ginormous supersized building covers an area of land measuring 454,000 square metres (4.89 million sq ft.) which is about the same size as the Vatican City - an actual country.

But what industry would need a building the size of a country?

The building is the Bloemenveiling Aalsmeer (Aalsmeer Flower Auction). Every day over 20 million flowers come here from all over the world to be traded and then shipped on again to customers in Europe and the World. The UK cut flower market, for example, is worth around $1.19 billion and around 80% of that comes via the Netherlands. Much of it from that single building.

Flowers are big business. Ask any florist on Valentine's Day. But how planet worthy is this seemingly 'natural' industry when a rose is grown in a faraway continent, on land that used to grow food, then chopped from its roots, expensively sent by plane to a country on another continent, traded, and then trucked to yet another country. All so people can spend hard earned money to give it to someone else.

Then, after all of that, they can enjoy the pleasure of watching it decay and die over the next week or so? Even more unnatural is that the same flower could have been grown in your own garden or sourced from a floriculturist ('flower farmer' = who knew?) in your own area.

A 'rose by any other name' wrote Shakespeare - that other name today should be 'crazy'.

If you are tempted to give flowers as a gift then it may well be worth keeping the actual gesture - but buying the flowers before they are decapitated - when they are still growing and can remain that way for very long periods of time. The common name for these are ... yes ... plants, as in planted in something, like the ground or a pot. Why not keep them that way?

People stuck to the flower gifting idea who want to send, say, roses on Valentine's Day, can instead buy a single rose instead of a dozen. This isn't just a one-twelfth reduction in price, but one-twelfth reduction in aircraft, truck and refrigeration emissions transporting the roses from farms in places like Ecuador to Miami (where 90% of the 1.3 billion imported roses enter the US). Roses can triple in price on Valentine's Day so that $20 plus saving (in a typical US flower shop) could even be used to have a tree planted in a loved ones honour.

A Valentines tree may sound nuts. But norms change. Especially if they make sense. It wasn't even 100 years ago that people bought heroin from pharmacies as cold medicine, all movies were black and white, seatbelts were seen as dangerous, people wore fancy dress on Thanksgiving not Halloween, the USA didn't have an official national anthem - or 50 stars, and, in the UK, women under 30 couldn't vote

Houseplants are the most logical, environmental, visual, and healthy replacement for cut flowers. Among the many good reasons to give them over cut flowers, the simplest is that they release oxygen into our homes. The best reason, however, comes from NASA, whose research on breathable atmospheres helped them discover that certain plants can remove as much as 87% of toxins from the air in a room, in less than a day. Houseplants, combined with open windows and natural potpourri, are also cheaper and more pleasant than potentially hazardous chemical emitting air fresheners.

Impact: Reduce unnecessary global 'flower flights' by up to 91%.
Difficulty: Easy, but culturally hard.
Money-saving: Yes £10+
Action: Choose plants over flowers, or buy locally grown flowers where possible.

I Do This Already  **I Choose This Task** ☐

Work from Home (or Cafe, Beach, Park) For at Least Half of Your Time

There is a group of people in the USA who spend over three hours most days going to and from work. These 'extreme commuters' aren't some minor group of over enthusiastic employees, they number about one in ten (9.8%) of the 148 million US workers who commute to a workplace. That's 15.1 million people - or more than live in each one of 46 of the 50 US states - collectively wasting 11.8 billion hours of potential work time each year.

The average American worker, however, has a commuting time from home to work of 27.6 minutes. Which, according to the US Census Bureau is a new high for the country - and an extra 2.6 minutes per commute from 15 years ago. In the European Union, the average commute is 25 minutes, while in the UK it is 30 minutes. And that's just one way - they do virtually the same thing, but backwards, later that day.

In the USA, most commuters get to and from work in cars, with 119 million Americans (80.4%) driving alone and 14 million (9.5%) sharing a car. The other common means of transportation to work are walking (4.1m), bus (3.6m), subway (2.9m), and long distance or commuter train (1.0m). Only 800,000 commuters cycle to work, while the rest use all manner of transport from motorbikes to streetcars, taxis, even horses or skis.

If we take a step back from this daily grind we can see, that for most of us, the technology is fully in place so we don't need to make a commute at all. We can, and many already have, adapted our lives so, our office can be in the most logical place - at home - or anywhere our laptop or phone is turned on.

Working from home, or remote working as it is often termed, has an incredible number of advantages other than simply losing the commute, saving transport costs, and adding an extra hour to your day. If organised well, for employees, it offers flexibility with regard to time, gives a renewed sense of responsibility, allows people to concentrate on their job, escapes the office politics, evades the dress code, provides a healthier environment, and simply allows people to work in balance with their personal lives for things like childcare, medical appointments, meal times, etc.

For employers, the benefits include massively reduced need for workspace and associated costs such as heating and parking spaces, increased productivity, less days lost to sickness, increased retention of staff, and flexibility (for example, staff choosing to work early mornings or late evenings to deal with time zone differences). The biggie though is profit, with at least one survey suggesting each remote worker is 21% more profitable than those based purely at the workplace.

That said, the biggest winner from people working from home is the environment. In the USA alone, if half of the 148 million commuters suddenly began working from home, that would mean at least 60 million cars off the road for one hour a day. Over a year that would equate to around 15.6 billion hours of driving not happening. At just 20mph commuting speed and 24.9 miles per gallon that would mean 12.53 billion gallons of fuel not used - a figure just under the 14.72 billion gallons of all US imports of oil from Persian Gulf countries.

Remote working is not for everyone, but if you have a role where you can stop, or at least reduce by half, working at an office, you can make a massive difference to the planet, your health, your pocket and your family.

Impact: Could reduce rush hour traffic emissions by up to half
Difficulty: Initially difficult to set up
Money-saving: Yes £500+
Action: Decide to work away from office half the time. Make it happen.

I Do This Already  **I Choose This Task**

Don't be a Douche! Shower in Less than Five Minutes

The average time spent in the shower in the USA, Canada and UK is eight minutes, while in Australia it's seven minutes. The average shower in France is reported as being higher at nine minutes (although a 2015 survey found the actual frequency of daily showers in France was only 57%, compared to 85% in neighbouring countries Germany and the UK).

In most of the world women out-shower men. One notable exception is the ancestral home of the Vikings, Sweden, where a 2005 survey showed men took more showers than women.

Most of the world prefers a shower in the morning, while in China and Brazil the preferred time is in the evening.

Showering is a big part of our day. It makes us clean, refreshed, and ready for the day (or evening) ahead.

All showers, and all baths, are different in design, size, water flow, etc., but one thing that normally holds true throughout the world is that having a shower tends to use a third less water than taking a bath.

The average shower uses around 12 litres (3.17 gallons) of water per minute. If the average time in the shower is eight minutes, that means 96 litres (25.36 gallons) of water will be used. A typical bath uses 132 litres (34.87 gallons).

If you live in a place which experiences water-stress, such as California or Cape Town, then reducing the time you are in the shower from eight to five minutes or less will save around 36 litres of water - or 11 times as much water as adult humans are recommended to drink every day. It will also save you 37.5% of the cost, and environmental impact, of heating the shower.

Five minutes in the shower, instead of being under the water for a longer period, is also more beneficial for the skin. Overly long periods, anything over ten minutes, can end up removing too many of the skin's natural oils which leads to de-moisturising. This is especially so if the water is too hot.

Changing a showering habit from where it is now (average 8 minutes) to one that is less than five minutes may seem like an easy thing to do, especially as most people mistakenly believe they take five minutes already. But it is a remarkably hard move.

The first, and simplest thing to do is to hit a timer as you go in a shower to see what your regular time is already. Most likely, because you know it is an experiment, you will probably move a little quicker than normal, but at least you have a figure. If it is less than five minutes, well done, you're already there. If it is a figure over five minutes you will understand what time you need to shave off and can use a timer to stay on target.

If you are a lover of music while you shower, then pick a track, or a couple of tracks that amount to five minutes. While you shower you will know you have until the songs end to finish your 'ablutions' (lovely word, Latin origin, meaning 'wash away'). Among the 5-minute-ish timed songs to choose are Mr Blue Sky by ELO (5.06 mins), Smells Like Teen Spirit by Nirvana (5.01 mins), Billie Jean by Michael Jackson, and Morning Glory by Oasis (5.03 mins). Songs to avoid are Bohemian Rhapsody by Queen at nearly six minutes and Voodoo Chile by Jimi Hendrix at 15 minutes.

If you want to stay in the shower longer but still use less water, then you can employ an old navy trick. The so-called Navy Shower. Simply turn the water down, or off, during the long bit of the shower where you are lathering.

Impact: Saves up to 37.5% of water used.
Difficulty: Easy to start. Hard to maintain.
Money-saving: Yes £50+
Action: Set a timer at shower time or get the music playing.

I Choose This Task ☐

Pick up Litter like the Swedish Do Plogg and be Fit

The list of top twenty most popular sports on the planet would certainly include football, tennis, golf, darts, rugby, cricket, baseball, all invented in the UK, plus American football, volleyball and basketball, all invented in the USA (although the last one was invented by a Canadian). The list would most probably not include Floorball, Table Hockey, Kubb, Rink Bandy, and Sledge Hockey - the five most well-known sports invented in Sweden.

Sweden is a sporty nation. Behind only Finland, Hungary, Bahamas, and Bermuda, in having the fifth highest ratio of Olympic gold medals to the size of its population, but it never created a sport that became a truly massive global hit.

One Swede, a man by the name of Erik Ahlström, is possibly going to change all this - and all because he moved house.

In 2016, Mr Ahlström had returned to the capital, Stockholm, after living in a small skiing community called Åre, close to the Norwegian border. He had been away for twenty years and became immediately struck with how dirty and full of litter the city had become. He took ownership of the problem and simply started picking up litter, whether he was cycling, walking or jogging. Within a short period, he began running with friends, all carrying bags, and they would include picking up litter as a way of providing variation in their body movements. The Swedish for 'pick up' is 'plocka upp', which combined with 'jogging' quickly became 'plogging'. A new sporting activity had arrived.

It did not take long until the craze of 'plogging' had literally swept the streets of Sweden clean. Sport and the environment had come together.

Today, people are plogging, some competitively, in over 100 countries.

Litter is not just unpleasant, it has been, and continues to be, the cause of injury, displacement, and death, direct or indirect, of literally millions of humans and billions of other forms of life on land and sea. In 2002, for example, over 500 people died in floods that covered a third of Bangladesh. Leaving 4.7 million people displaced. It was discovered that the problem was aggravated by drains clogged with plastic bags. That country quickly became the first in the world to announce a plastic bag ban. As for wildlife, most have seen pictures of dead seals, swans and other animals tangled in plastic and other littered items. What most people don't realise is that even when that animal has decomposed the plastic is then free to do the same thing again.

Pick up litter wherever you can. Even if it's not your own. Litter is not always purposely thrown away by the anti-social, but more likely to be ignorantly dropped, left, mislaid, or forgotten and then blown about. One survey suggests that almost 20% is blown off or out of vehicles or unsecured rubbish bins.

Globally, the common causes of litter are smoking (cigarette butts are the number one litter item), construction sites, carelessness, and lack of recycling/rubbish bins. A general increase in litter also occurs when people can visibly see other litter, or there is a lack of litter education. Low fines for littering and a visible inaction from authority are also big factors.

Litter is a shameful reminder of how far down a place, and its people, has dropped. But if we understand that each individual is inadvertently the cause of a minimum of 10 pieces of litter each year, then it is our problem to solve. If just one in five of us went 'plogging' each week on a walk, jog or cycle, picking up just one single item, this would result in zero litter.

Bonus point: Plogging uses 106 more calories per hour than normal jogging.

Impact: Could potentially remove all litter from our streets.
Difficulty: Easy and healthy.
Money-saving: No, but occasionally, ploggers do find money.
Action: Go plog!

I Do This Already  **I Choose This Task** ☐

Shut Your Mouth! There is Plastic in most Chewing Gum

One of world's weirdest tourist attractions is Gum Wall, found in downtown Seattle in Washington, USA. A 50 foot long wall made up of chewed gum placed there by literally thousands of visitors over the years. Unsurprisingly, it was voted the second 'germiest' tourist attraction on the planet (first place was Ireland's 'kiss it' Blarney Stone). The gum is inches thick in places and you know you're close to the attraction before you see it - so strong is it's gummy smell.

We love chewing gum. From images of legendary football manager Alex Ferguson literally chewing his way through every Manchester United game, to stars such as Doris Day, Arnold Schwarzenegger, Meryl Streep, Jodie Foster and Gwyneth Paltrow shown in iconic pictures blowing bubble gum bubbles. Britney Spears old disposed gum was even auctioned on eBay in 2004 (sold at $140). It is no surprise that the chewing gum industry, worldwide, is estimated to be worth $29.9 billion a year.

Chewing gum is everywhere, literally, from stuck on our sidewalks, found under school desks, even taken to the Moon. David Beckham unroyally chewed away in church while attending the Royal Wedding of Harry and Meghan and talent show judge Sharon Osbourne famously spat hers out on the red carpet at the Daytime Emmy Awards.

Sadly, as much joy as we get from chewing gum, the downside is that most of us don't realise the majority of brands contain plastic. You are literally chewing the same stuff as food bags, or kids glue, or what car tyres are made from. Even worse, unless we dispose of it properly we are causing a massive microplastic problem for the future.

Proper disposal of chewing gum does not mean swallowing and thinking the issue is done. The old wives' tale about it staying in your stomach for 7 years is not true - although there have been rare cases where it has helped cause intestine blockages. Most chewing gum, because its gum base is made from plastics, will not break down in your digestive system. This means it can take the journey through your body in around 1 to 3 days and then return to potentially create a problem down the line - the sewer line - as chewing gum is found in almost every 'fatberg' blocking our city sewers.

Most chewing gum is not biodegradable or easily recyclable so ends up in a trash bin, which then ends up in landfill, or burned to make energy, and more CO_2.

The biggest problem with untrashed chewing gum spat onto a street is not just that it is visually unpleasant, costs around one dollar per person each year to clear, or people can get it stuck to their feet or clothes, it's that it will eventually erode into micro plastics and end up in our oceans where it creates a whole range of different planet killing problems.

There are solutions. The most obvious is to work out whether you are happy chewing on flavoured plastic and then decide to stop altogether (there are many alternatives) or to only purchase chewing gum made from ingredients that are biodegradable, like chicle, the natural gum base made from the sap of the sapodilla tree found in Mexico - and the original ingredient of gum before companies found it cheaper to use plastic.

If you choose to stay part of the problem then there are areas of the world that have 'gumdrop' recycling bins. These are for used chewing gum and, get this, actually made from recycled chewing gum, that is then used to make more recycling bins for chewing gum - or products like shoe soles or phone covers.

Impact: Reduces future microplastics.
Difficulty: Moderately easy.
Money-saving: Yes. £5+
Action: Stop eating chewing gum or change to non-plastic brand.

I Choose This Task

Treat Your Dishes Like Fishes Love Your Dishwasher

Aretha Franklin, often called the 'Queen of Soul' famously sang a song with Annie Lennox of the Eurthymics which included the line 'we're coming out of the kitchen, cause there's something we forgot to say to you ....'

The rest of the line, and the actual title of the song, was 'Sisters Are Doin' It For Themselves'.

The song was written in 1985, one century after another 'sister', Josephine Cochrane, of Shelby, Illinois, had also done something very much for herself - and something that gave everybody a reason not to spend too much time in the kitchen at all. She invented the world's first commercially successful dishwasher. Cochrane was initially inspired to create her invention to reduce the chances of breakage of her own fine china rather than save time. But, even though the dishwasher was hand cranked, it was still much faster than standing by a sink with a scrubbing brush in hand.

Josephine Shelby is almost always seen in any list of great women inventors. One of the great female icons. Seldom, if at all, is she noted as one of the great environmentalists. This should be corrected because her machine, and the many different makes of dishwashers invented afterwards nearly all use water pressure to clean - and this generally means a massive reduction in water usage.

Numerous reports and surveys over the years have consistently noted that using a dishwasher to clean our pots, pans, cutlery and dishes is, on average, five times more efficient at saving water than hand washing. This figure can go to ten times more efficient if there is a full load on a light or eco setting in a large dishwasher.

To put this into context, if we take one of Scotland's most famous tourist attractions, Loch Ness, it is so big (56km2) and so deep (230m) that it contains more water than in all the lakes in neighbouring England and Wales put together. No wonder it is difficult to find its most famous resident - the Loch Ness Monster. Even so, its 7,452 billion litres of water could be emptied in 67 years if everyone in Scotland used it to hand wash their dishes every day. This could be a far longer 335 years if an efficient dishwasher was used.

Looking at dishwashers from a water saving angle it is far better to use them over hand washing if people live in an area where water needs to be conserved. However, if people are not in an area of water stress then it might be worthwhile concentrating on the energy needed to power the dishwasher to help the environment.

One simple method of saving energy is to simply fill a sink, or bucket, with cold water and put plates, pans, cups and cutlery in the water throughout the day. The soaking process alone, or 'treating dishes like fishes', should remove most of the dirt. This means, when they are put in the dishwasher, a lower setting can be used. Using the most energy-efficient setting this can mean a reduction in energy (and cost) of 20%.

Forget the numerous advertisements pushing images of mums and daughters (or dads and sons) happily hand washing their dishes together while discussing how soft it makes their hands feel. That image omits the reality that only 3% of the world's water is freshwater - and only one-sixth of that freshwater is accessible - so wasting five times as much at a laborious kitchen sink is far less happy than simply loading a dishwasher together, then zipping out of the kitchen to enjoy a life.

Impact: Save five times as much fresh water when cleaning pots and pans.
Difficulty: Easy.
Money-saving: Yes £10+
Action: Use a dishwasher over hand washing.

I Do This Already  **I Choose This Task** ☐

Use Your Money as a Voting Card

If you live in New Zealand and love football you have probably heard of former midfielder Tim Brown, who played 30 games for his national team until retiring in 2012. If you're not from New Zealand you may not know him as a footballer at all, but as the co-founder of a very on-trend footwear brand called Allbirds - a company that didn't exist until 2016 but is now valued, at the time of writing, at $2.1 billion.

Hard work and good marketing aside, the reason the brand went from zero to billions is simple, people liked the product. They liked the very green idea behind the product, and liked the fact it was a good alternative to the mostly synthetic products that already existed in that market.

Their first product was a running shoe made mostly from renewable materials such as merino wool and castor bean oil. The product also came in a recycled card shoebox which also doubled as the delivery box. Anyway, before we all turn into fanboys and fangirls, it is important to note this isn't an ad for Allbirds, but simply an example of what can happen when people really get behind an idea that helps the environment - with their own hard-earned money. And people did exactly that, with Barack Obama and Oprah Winfrey among their earliest customers.

On the flipside, the world's largest ever marine oil pollution incident, the Deepwater Horizon oil spill in the Gulf of Mexico in 2010, had the knock-on effect of such great public anger, it nearly bankrupted BP, the company who operated the oil rig. The company suffered a boycott and protests at their filling stations, before eventually paying out $65 billion in compensation.

Using our money, almost like a voting card, to endorse or remove our support for a product, thing, or idea, that helps or harms the environment, is not a new concept, but can be very effective.

The 1974 hit song *For The Love Of Money* by the O'Jays, has a super catchy line, 'Money, Money Money - Some People Got To Have it' and it was used very effectively as the theme tune for the US version of the TV series The Apprentice. The line after that is the more fascinating though, 'Do Things, Do Things, Do Bad Things With It', and this is where anyone with any care for the environment should take notice. In effect, the song highlights the reality that some people will do anything to make money, even bad things.

Of course, as human beings who care for our planet, we should make sure that anyone making money makes it by taking good, rather than bad, options. And there is a nice way for us to guide more ethical behaviour.

Think of every dollar, pound, rupee, rand, dong, euro, or any other currency you own as a micro voting card. If there are two products, why not use your money to vote for the product that is most beneficial for the environment. If the product is not beneficial, don't vote for it, and let them know you're not voting for it, by simply not spending your hard-earned cash on their stuff.

Money is an incredibly brilliant motivator, up there with love or fear. As soon as a company finds the money tap they rely on is being turned off by you and other people like you, because their products are ecologically wrong, they will soon change their ways, or risk going bust.

Put simply, you work hard for your money. So, you and only you, not others marketing and PR departments, should decide whether to give it to polluters, resource abusers, unmotivated corporations, fossil fuel pushers, or banks, who use it to fund planet crushing projects for the sake of their profits.

Naturally, if you really like things that benefit the environment, show the true might of the mighty dollar, the powerful pound, or the energetic euro. Give them some green for being green!

Impact: Significant in making companies go greener.
Difficulty: Easy.
Money-saving: Yes-No-Maybe.
Action: Have an awareness of all items you purchase and how green or ethical they are.

I Do This Already  **I Choose This Task**

Grow Stuff

There is a chance that, unless you are over the age of 50 or watched a lot of old TV with your grandparents when you were a child, you may never have heard of Richard Briers (1934-2013). A fabulously funny British actor, he starred in a 1970s BBC TV comedy series *The Good Life* about a 40 year-old man called Tom Good who, with wife Barbara (Felicity Kendal), decide to quit the 'rat race' and their jobs, and turn their suburban London home into a self-sufficient paradise, much to the dismay of their middle-class neighbours.

The series was a winner, with viewing figures of 18 million in the UK. It was popular in Canada, Australia, New Zealand, Belgium, Finland, the Netherlands, and even the USA, where it was retitled *Good Neighbors* and shown on PBS.

The series is notable because it helped bring back the idea of self-sufficiency, growing things, make and mend, and simple pleasures, to a generation of people who, like the rest of the Post-War world of the mid-1970s, had become accustomed to convenience, gadgets, and the 9-5 of life.

In a small way, *The Good Life* spurred many around the world to have a go at a greener life, growing their own food, even making beer, wine and clothes.

In real life, Richard Briers, didn't particularly like his very likeable character, accusing him after the series ended of being 'very selfish' and 'obsessed' with his plans. In a way this is understandable, many greens are a bit over the top, tree-huggy, and boring. Briers generation ran counter to this - they simply didn't grow stuff themselves - that was for others to do.

Today, the UK, where the series was set, barely produces one-quarter of its own fruit and vegetables - the rest coming from vast distances overseas. It is vital, even in a small way, that we find our inner cheerful Tom Good, get out into the garden, allotment, balcony or window box - and grow stuff.

There are 7.9 billion people on the planet and collectively we share 2.3 billion households. Each housing an average of 3.4 people, dotted everywhere from Afghanistan to Zimbabwe. The amount of land on the planet is 149 million square kilometres (57.5 million square miles), which works out at 36.8 billion acres. Shared by everyone on Earth this would mean 4.66 acres each, or close to 16 acres if shared by households.

The amount of land a family of four need to become self-sufficient varies widely, but most estimates are around 2 acres. The things that change the estimates up or down are variables such as quality of land, climate, rainfall/water, hilly/flat, sun/shade, what food will be grown, how much people eat and whether they will share, barter or sell produce with others.

Self-sufficiency is not for everyone, but growing a few items in your garden, even herbs in your kitchen, is very easily achievable - and makes a difference. If half of every garden in the UK was planted with things like apples, plums, tomatoes, potatoes, salads and the like, then the country could produce more fruit and vegetables than it presently imports each year.

Five or six large pots filled with different lettuce seeds can provide salads for half a year (or longer if grown under glass). Fruit trees can grow up walls and give an endless, but seasonal, supply of apples, pears, plums, etc. Potatoes and tomatoes grow easily. Strawberries and raspberries need little care. People can even grow grapes - all for less effort than 30 minutes a day.

If there is really no space, or not enough space, then community gardens are an option. Most are on common land or allotments but some are even on train stations. A couple of enjoyable hours a week working alongside neighbours and you have got veggies and salads for most of the year.

Impact: Reduces need to remove more forest for farming.
Difficulty: Moderately easy.
Money-saving: Yes £100+
Action: Buy seeds, plant seeds, water plants, watch plants grow, eat crops.

I Choose This Task

Maintain Your Stuff

During its history, there have been many disasters leading to massive loss of life in the USA. The biggest in terms of sheer numbers have been epidemics, such as the 1918 Spanish Flu, HIV/AIDS, and Covid-19, all of which have killed over half a million Americans each - a figure higher than the 418,800 who died in World War Two. Coincidentally, another pandemic, the 1958 Asian flu pandemic, killed almost the same number as the 116,708 who died in World War One. Deaths from natural disasters, such as the 8,000 who died in the 1900 Galveston Hurricane or the 3,000 who died in the 1906 San Francisco Earthquake are also high on the list. Two disasters never forgotten are the Japanese attack on Pearl Harbor in 1941, killing 2,467 people and the September 11 attacks of 2001 when 2,996 people were murdered by terrorists in New York, Washington DC, and Pennsylvania.

The two biggest 'accidents' in US history, however, are not quite so well remembered. The first, the Johnstown Flood of 1889, killed 2,208 people in Pennsylvania, when the South Fork Dam suffered a catastrophic collapse. The second, the sinking of the steamboat Sultana on the Mississippi River in 1865 occurred after the boilers of the massively overloaded ship blew up while close to Memphis, Tennessee, killing 1,700. The dam collapse killed a similar number to American combat deaths in the War of 1812 and the ship explosion killed more people than died on the Titanic. Yet, they are side notes in history.

These accidents were massive and should be remembered forever, not just for the loss, but by what binds them together, the fact they were a result, in part, of simple bad maintenance. Stupidly, the dam had been lowered and had pipes removed for scrap, while the ship's boiler had a quick patch up earlier in the day because proper repair would take too long.

If you want to help the planet then one of the simplest ways is to take care of what you've already got. Yes - your stuff. Love it. Appreciate what it does for you and, above all, keep it maintained. Keep it clean, keep it oiled, keep it dry, keep it in whatever condition is recommended, and there are likely to be financial savings and benefits, personal pride, and an environmental spin-off to your actions.

If you own a car, as an example, it is worth noting that a zero or badly maintained car will certainly make your vehicle less efficient. The professional estimate is a loss of 20% in fuel efficiency, which translates as paying for £1 of fuel and only getting 80p worth of bang. A zero or badly maintained car is also 15% more prone to needing unnecessary repairs and/or a 15% increase in servicing costs.

A zero or badly maintained item, be it a car, a ladder, a gas heater, a power tool, or a million other things, is also more likely to kill you than one that is properly maintained. A heartbreaking example is the one in six fire deaths in the USA where a smoke alarm was present at a fire but didn't activate.

An unsharpened blade makes a job longer and takes more energy to complete. Maintain stuff. Either through people who know what they are doing, or learn yourself. Expert videos are everywhere to help.

A healthy mantra to adopt is: 'If it's maintained it's less likely to break - If it's breaking, repair - If it can't be repaired, replace - If you can't get the same - upgrade - or borrow - or live without'.

Becoming a maintainer rather than a constant upgrader is such a simple change of attitude but will save thousands of dollars/pounds/euros - and every year that you get to keep an item means an extra year it doesn't need to be replaced using valuable resources, then packaged, then transported.

Impact: Can reduce your personal vehicle emissions by 20%.
Difficulty: Easy, but requires work.
Money-saving: Yes £500+
Action: Treat everything you own with respect, and maintain regularly.

I Choose This Task

Ask Your Energy Supplier to Supply You with 100% Renewable Energy

Possibly one of the most amazing facts to ever enter the realm of human knowledge was discovered from a survey of 1500 parents in the UK in 2017 which found they face an average of 73 questions from their young children every day. That's an incredible 26,663 questions a year.

This may be a long shot for parents, but if one of those questions is ever about the Statue of Liberty there is some information you may like to have at hand. First, the quite sombre and masculine looking face of the Statue of Liberty was based on Augusta Bartholdi, the mother of its energetic French sculptor, Frederic Auguste Bartholdi. Second, the Statue is really tall, from toe to torch it measures 151 feet (46m) which is the size of 46 average four year olds standing on top of each other. Third, and most cool, the statue isn't even half as tall as just one of the blades on the latest generation of modern wind turbines.

Tenuous link aside, wind turbines are getting bigger, and more powerful. At the Port of Rotterdam in the Netherlands a Haliade-X wind turbine stands 814ft (248m) high. One single revolution of its 351ft (107m) blades can supply enough energy to power a typical Dutch house for two days.

More interestingly, just one of these wind turbines can save up to 52,000 metric tons of CO2 - or to put it in plain English, the same amount of emissions as created by 11,000 vehicles in one year.

Another renewable energy, solar power, is the most abundant natural energy source on the planet. According to the US Dept of Energy some 173,000 terawatts of solar energy strike the Earth at any one moment. This is over 10,000 times more energy than the world uses in total.

With so much abundant renewable energy available to the world in the form of wind power, solar, hydro, geothermal, and tidal, plus the less green biomass and nuclear energy sources, it seems unimaginably stupid that we continue to use the fossil fuels of coal, oil and gas to power our world. This free renewable energy is literally in the air, the sun, our land and our water - all we have to do is decide to reach out and capture it.

Even more bizarre is that even though the costs of many renewable energy sources are now cheaper, we still persist in using fossil fuels - the very thing we know helped create the problem of climate change in the first place - and the thing that , if we are not careful, will make climate change speed up and destroy the planet we know.

According to the US Environmental Protection Agency (EPA) the burning of fossil fuels for electricity and heat is the single largest source (25%) of greenhouse gas emissions.

One of the single greatest things a person can do to change this for good is also one of the simplest. Contact your electricity supplier and ask to go on a 100% renewable energy source for all your energy. In an instant you have made your home part of the solution, not the problem.

In many countries changing from a 'standard' to a '100% renewable' plan is as simple as one click on a website. If your electricity supplier makes it difficult, then, if possible, change your supplier to one that makes it easy.

A world run by renewable energy may seem a million miles away but it is achievable quite quickly. In 2011, renewable energy provided 37% of the energy used in Scotland. Today, that figure has increased to over 97% and the nation no longer uses coal-fired power stations. Consumer demand for renewable energy was a significant factor in making the change.

Impact: Removes the single largest home source of greenhouse gas emissions.
Difficulty: Moderately easy.
Money-saving: Yes-No-Maybe.
Action: Contact electricity supplier and ask for a 100% renewable energy contract.

I Do This Already  **I Choose This Task**

Can't Recycle It? Send it Back

The highest paid television presenter on the BBC is the former England football captain Gary Lineker - even after he took a well-publicised pay cut. Great presenter, super charming, knowledgeable, OBE off the Queen, Golden Boot award at the World Cup in Mexico in 1986, and has a particular record that is the equivalent, in football terms, of being a saint - he never received a red or yellow card in any of the 16 years he played professional football.

We mention this English national hero because of one thing - he has been the face of an American owned crisps brand in the UK for over a quarter of a century and has appeared in over 150 of their adverts. This lucrative relationship hardly troubled the public except for a twitter spat with another TV presenter, Piers Morgan, who wrote: 'Mate, you flog (sell) crisps to kids when Britain has the worst child obesity rates in Europe, and flog (sell) them in plastic bags that destroy the planet'.

Without getting too deep into the spat, the reality was that the crisps company had just been the target of a campaign by environmentalists to highlight the fact that the 11 million crisp packets a day it produced could not be taken at most recycling centres, other than as landfill or incineration, and that crisp packets dating from forty years earlier were still being found floating in rivers and seas, and dug up in gardens and wilderness.

The campaign, which ended with a commitment by the company to change their packaging within seven years (and have collection points for packaging now), simply involved people posting the empty packs to the company and suggesting: 'It's your packaging. You caused the problem. Sort it'.

If you want to reduce the amount of packaging that ends up littering and polluting our planet then the most obvious thing to do is not to buy any products that have unnecessary or non-recyclable packaging. This also has the benefit of hitting company profits which itself will most likely initiate change. In reality, on planet real world, sometimes we find ourselves in a situation where we are compelled to take the packaging, such as when we desperately need a particular product or we need to keep the product clean or fresh and have no other means of doing so.

If you find yourself at home with a piece of packaging that you discover cannot be normally recycled, then make this your problem - you bought it and you are responsible for it.

The first responsible thing to do is to ask the company, either by phone call, e-mail, website chatbox, or more publicly for the benefit of others, via their social media pages, whether it can actually be recycled.

If the answer is yes, ask where, and how, and follow their recycling advice. If the recycling method is way too complex ask them why they use this packaging and will it always be like that. If the answer is ambiguous, advise you will send it directly to them so they can sort it. Don't be afraid to ask for a return merchandise authorisation (minus product) or a freepost address.

If the answer is no, it cannot be recycled, ask why not, then ask what methods they are employing to change the situation. Once again, if the answer is vague or ambiguous, simply send it to the head of the company and politely request that, as they created this problem, could they sort it out - and could they reply with a copy of their company environment policy. If this happens regularly enough things will soon change.

Impact: Massive reduction in unrecyclable packaging.
Difficulty: Easy, but time consuming.
Money-saving: No.
Action: Share at #RecyclingingProbs if you come across any packaging that can't be recycled.

I Choose This Task

Swap Your Wardrobe The Easy Way to Get New Clothes

The oil industry is the world's largest source of pollution, while surprisingly, the second largest, according to Greenpeace, is the fashion industry.

Hollywood will now certainly have to change its ideas of how our planet will be destroyed. No longer by laughing Martians, asteroids, zombies, shady arms dealers, religious fanatics, fallen superheroes, or rogue politicians - the new destroyers are much more interesting. They are an army of supermodels and their weapon of mass destruction is ... the catwalk.

In reality, the big problem is not the whole fashion industry, which will come as some relief to Naomi, Cindy, Kate, Claudia, and Cara, but one aspect of it - fast fashion - the cheap mass production of 'in then out of season' clothes.

To say the world buys close to 100 billion items of clothing every year is just a number. But if we visualise the figures we can better see the scale of the issue. That 100 billion works out at almost 13 items for every person on the planet. More than one item every month. Double the amount we bought at the start of the century/millennium. Which itself was double what we bought in 1980. The craziness of fast fashion consumption is best noted in a news story from 2011 which noted the average woman in the UK bought half her own body weight in clothes - every year.

A simple pair of jeans and a shirt, weighing 1kg of cotton, can take up to 20,000 litres of water to produce - and cotton has half the carbon footprint of polyester. Even worse, according to a UK parliamentary report, by 2030 fast fashion is expected to need 35% more land - an extra 115 million hectares - which is bigger than the whole of France and Spain combined.

There are solutions to fast fashion. One of the simplest ways of not seeing the planet eat up another area the size of Jamaica every year just to make clothes, is to ignore fashion trends and stick with what you've already got. More fun, however, is to swap your wardrobe - or at least the estimated 44% of items the average person has not worn in the past year.

The human body shape generally comes in three versions, or more accurately 'somatotypes' (great word): ectomorph, mesomorph, and endomorph. In plain English, these are 'lean and thin', 'athletic', and 'large and fat'. We are then made up of numerous variations within these groups with some overlapping.

Clothes wise, this is great news, as even though we'd all like to think our bodies were totally unique, with 7.9 billion people on the planet, there are literally millions of people who are exactly the same shape as you.

These similar sized people will most probably (unless they live in a naturist colony) all have clothes as well - and all have unwanted clothes which they are prepared to swap. We know this is actually true because of the burgeoning market in clothes swapping. A market perfect for those who want to help the environment and maintain a sense of style.

The most traditional form of 'swapping' comes in organised meet-ups where people literally take their stuff to a common location and barter. More sophisticated are the online versions of the meet-ups, but there are also bespoke sites, normally with a small charge, where you send in your clothes, and a specialist collects a similar amount for you from stuff of the same size with your style in mind. Of course, everyone can simply buy or sell second hand clothes online or buy or give unwanted clothes to charity shops. Whichever route, it increases the life of clothes and, more importantly, says no to fast fashion.

Impact: Has potential to remove over 20% of effects of fast fashion.
Difficulty: Moderately easy, fun, and stylish.
Money-saving: Yes £100+
Action: Don't buy new clothes, swap the ones you don't want for ones you would like.

I Choose This Task ☐

Take the 'Cry' out of Cryptocurrency

The South American country of Argentina is really big. You could fit Israel in its borders 128 times, or 67 Switzerlands, or 11 UKs. Argentina is even four times bigger than Texas (and nowhere is bigger than Texas - ask any Texan).

Argentina is the birthplace of the tango and the modern ballpoint pen, famous for its magnificent wines and meat, has incredible scenery such as the Iguazu Falls and Patagonia, and has an absolute love of football (think Maradona, Messi and Aguero). It is also famed for Eva Peron, a woman so beloved that she was the subject of a globally popular musical and movie 'Evita'.

Argentina, and its 45 million people, play a major role in our world, and their efforts use up a lot of energy - over 122 terawatt-hours (TWh). But, here's the thing, in February 2021, the eighth largest country in the world used the same amount of electricity as the world used to power Bitcoin - a cryptocurrency. This is not so much 'Don't Cry For Me Argentina', as Evita might say, but more 'Don't Crypto For Me Like Argentina'.

Cryptocurrency is a world most people don't fully understand, even among those who invest in its 5,000 plus different forms such as BitCoin and Ethereum. Essentially it is a decentralised form of digital money that uses blockchain to operate. Blockchain is like an open ledger shared by all its users which can be viewed - but not changed or backdated. The problem of using blockchain for cryptocurrency is that, to ensure the system is not open to counterfeiting or corruption, most transactions are validated by its users through a series of cryptographic puzzles. It is the massive computer power needed for these puzzles that is causing an environmental problem.

We now live in a world where de-commissioned coal power stations, such as the Greenidge Generation Power facility on Lake Seneca in upstate New York, have been converted to run on another climate changing fossil-fuel, natural gas, and then commissioned again to produce electricity. The only exception is these power stations are primarily creating electricity to power bitcoin 'mining' operations. Mining is the name given to the largely unnecessary process of using computers to solve the cryptographic puzzles that are used as security before Bitcoin transactions can be verified.

In a nutshell, we are bringing back dead power stations to burn fossil fuels to create electricity to create virtual money! Not even George Orwell could have envisaged that when he was writing his dystopian novel Nineteen Eighty-Four.

The concept of blockchain is brilliant. It has so much great potential for solving environmental problems - such as creating 100% transparent supply chains so we can see where pollution is coming from, to creating tokens in exchange for items that can be recycled, to distributing energy supplies more efficiently.

Energy supplies powering cryptocurrencies come, in the main, from wherever electricity can be found at the cheapest rates. At the time of writing the biggest suppliers are the USA, Kazakhstan and Russia, with at least one report suggesting that at least 61% of all this energy came from fossil-fuelled sources. China had been the biggest supplier, but began a crackdown on cryptocurrency mining in late 2021.

If you do one thing for the environment, ditch the 'crypto' until you know it runs without 'mining' as part of its blockchain (which many now do) or at least until you know it runs 100% on renewable energy.

Impact: Removes fossil fuel from an Argentina sized amount of energy.
Difficulty: Moderately easy.
Money-saving: Yes-No-Maybe.
Action: Make a transfer of any fossil fuelled crypto money to other places.

I Choose This Task

Be Fitter and Richer Sell Your Car

In December 2020 a London coroner made legal history after a landmark decision on the death of a nine year old girl called Ella Adoo-Kissi-Debrah. He concluded the young girl's death seven years earlier was caused by severe asthma and air pollution exposure. She lived just 30 metres from the main London South Circular Road and had been exposed to levels of nitrogen dioxide way in excess of UK, European, and World Health Organization guidelines. In short, this precious child literally died from our traffic fumes.

There are 2.6 million cars registered in London, which works out at roughly one car for every two households. Yet, London has one of the most effective public transport systems on the planet and hundreds of miles of bespoke cycle paths and lanes. Also, the most common distance for people who live in London to walk to work is just 5km (3 miles). In reality, there are so many alternatives to driving in London that most of those 2.6 million cars don't need to be there.

If you live in a large and compact metropolis (think New York, San Francisco, Singapore, rather than the spacey Los Angeles or Brisbane), then one great way of helping the environment, reducing pollution, while saving a fortune and improving personal health, is to simply ditch the car altogether. This may sound nuts to people who live for their cars but it's not that difficult to do.

The simplest way to see if a no car life is feasible for you is to imagine that your car simply disappeared overnight. Not stolen (there's one less worry), but just didn't exist. Look at the benefits first and then work out how you could overcome any possible downsides of a car free life.

Not having your own car instantly opens up a completely new world - and this doesn't just mean you are less likely to worry about being done for drink-driving, getting involved in a road rage incident, crashing, running someone over or never being able to find a parking space. If done well, it can mean you acquire a more relaxed way of travelling, increased fitness, some serious financial savings, a lot less hassle, and a far happier planet.

No insurance costs, no car taxes, no petrol costs, no servicing costs, no MOT to pass, no lease or loan payments, no hefty deposit or purchase price, no ugly car air fresheners to buy, no car washing, no new tyres to buy, no punctures, no new bulbs to buy, no parking fees, no need for a car port, less need for a garage, no parking tickets, no car sales staff, less traffic wardens, no more designated driver or friend and family chauffeur, no petrol station chocolate temptation, no car toys, no car stickers, no arguing with the navigation system, no windscreen wash fill-ups, no wipers to buy, no breakdowns waiting for roadside assistance to turn up, no traffic jams, no oil change, no checking tyre pressure, no parking permits, no anti-freeze, no speeding fines, no driveway in your garden, and the list goes on.

The average cost of running even the most modest of cars each year is around £3200 in the UK. This is the equivalent of buying a new high quality bike in month one (with helmet), hiring a small car 10 weekends of the year, taking 200 minimum fare Uber rides, and banking £1000. You also get the added bonus of the money from selling your car and the increased fitness from cycling and walking (or running, scootering, skateboarding, etc.).

If this is not for you, then there are thousands of carsharing schemes available. Or you could buy a small electric car - and never overpollute the air again.

Impact: Collectively, could stop people dying from air pollution exposure.
Difficulty: Hard initially.
Money-saving: Yes £1000+
Action: Drive electric, or sell car and use alternative transport.

I Do This Already  **I Choose This Task**

Love Your Clothes Air if You Care

Possibly one of the most interesting women of the 20th century was a New Zealand born lady called Nancy Wake. Raised in Australia she trained as a nurse, moved to New York, then became a journalist in London before basing herself in Paris as a European correspondent in a time when 1930s Germany was flexing its Nazi muscle. She married a French industrialist, and after his death at the hands of the Germans in World War Two, found herself part of the British Special Operations Executive (SOE), conducting sabotage, reconnaissance and espionage actions in enemy territory. Several books have been written about her exploits but the one thing you need to know is that five different countries awarded her medals and honours for bravery.

If you ever wondered what happens to our heroes when they grow old then Agent 'Helene' as she was known, when in her early seventies, retired with her second husband, former RAF pilot John Foward, to a small town called Port Macquarie in Australia. They stayed there for 12 years, until his death, after 40 years of marriage, at which point she sold her medals and emigrated once again - to London - where she eventually died at the age of 98. What a life!

The reason for mentioning Nancy Wake is that people like her need to be remembered. She gave everything to help win a war she knew the world couldn't lose, seeing a husband and many friends die along the way. Second, until recently, she was one of the few famous things the world knew about the beautiful little Aussie town of Port Macquarie.

That changed recently when the town found fame once again. This time for something very different - a washing line - or to be more accurate, a world record 10.08 kilometre (6.26 miles) long washing line, pegged with 107,886 socks.

Washing lines are important - they can also help save the world - and Port Macquarie knows this.

The inventor of the first successful home electric clothes dryer was James Ross Moore, who grew up in Canada and North Dakota - places not famous for great winter drying. It was no surprise he called his machine the 'June Day' Dryer - the idea being his machine would replicate drying in summer conditions. That was in 1938, but people quickly forgot the invention was for times when a washing line couldn't be used - and it became an all year round machine.

Washing lines have been under sustained attack ever since. Some housing developments have contracts with homeowners stating they can't be erected in gardens. Some councils, especially those in tourist areas, even have bans on washing, such as towels and bikinis, being visible on balconies.

And why? Well, if you take the high ground, it's down to the idea of 'keeping up the appearance' of a place - and surely we all want to live somewhere nice. If you take the low ground, it's down to the marketing led notion that only the middle class can afford clothes driers - and washing lines are a sign of poverty.

Trivial as it all may seem, in countries like the USA, great battles have been fought so that 'Right to Dry' or 'Solar Access' legislation could be passed, allowing anyone to dry their clothes on a line without hindrance. At the last count, only 20 of the 50 US states have this legal right in their law books.

How people dry their clothes is important. It can take up to 5.8% of all household electricity consumption. A simple outside clothes line replacing a dryer can reduce that massive energy demand - and save money.

Cutting back on a clothes dryer also has benefits beyond helping the environment. Line dried clothes have far less wear and tear so tend to last longer. They are also less prone to shrinkage.

Impact: Reduce up to 5.8% of all household electricity consumption.
Difficulty: Moderately easy.
Money-saving: Yes £100+
Action: Put up clothes line and attempt to use dryer less than 20 times a year.

I Do This Already  **I Choose This Task**

Buy Food for You - Not the Bin Save a Third of Your Food Costs

The United States Food & Drug Administration (FDA) suggests that the average American will throw away about a third of their food. Added together, this means food worth over $161 billion is thrown away in the United States each year.

The average farm in the USA is 444 acres in size and there are, at the last count, 2,023,400 of them dotted from the arctic cold of northern Alaska to the tropical tip of southern Florida. To put this wasted food in context, this would be the equivalent of taking the entire produce of 674,467 of those American farms and simply driving it straight to landfill. Forget the fact it took months to grow, had to be harvested, sorted, driven around, packaged, driven around again, put on supermarket shelves, promoted or advertised, sold, accounted, driven home, refrigerated or stored - then ignored, dumped and now makes methane under some once lovely valley, or smoke from some waste incineration unit.

Worse still, the wasted food took 299,463,348 acres of land to grow, which is 467,911 square miles, which itself is almost all the land in three Californias.

The main reasons for such abhorrent waste is four-fold: We food shop with eyes bigger than our stomachs. We don't plan meals. We don't know how to store food properly, and we don't understand food expiration dates.

A lack of clear labelling also has an impact, so we end up with things like 'best by', use by', 'sell by', 'freeze-by', 'expires', etc., and we have food makers and food suppliers whose main role is to make a profit for their shareholders. So they have less interest in wasted food than say your mum would if she knew you threw one bag of food in every three you buy straight into the bin.

The most obvious way to reduce this problem is to plan meals ahead rather than just 'go buy stuff'. In a world where one in every seven adults is classed as obese, the use of a nutritional plan, weekly, daily, or otherwise, is a good thing - for the individual and the environment.

Buying food immediately after you've just eaten is a good way of reducing overbuying food, thus causing waste. Reading labels on products (and taking glasses with you to supermarkets) also helps as it ensures food bought is what you and your family, and friends, are not allergic to - and actually like.

Food storage, and handling food quickly from store to fridge/ freezer also makes a difference. That smoked salmon may not be so appealing if its in the car on a hot day for longer than it needs to get home. Equally, a good fridge and freezer, and an actual cool dark storage area can make a big difference to the condition of your food and the duration period it can be stored.

Incredibly, not every country has a legal requirement for 'use by' dates on foods. The USA for example only has Federal Law stating 'use by' dates should be used for infant formula. Everything else is left to a voluntary system or individual states making their own laws. One great way of not wasting food is to know that 'best if used by' is not the same as 'use by' - the first means the food will stay at its optimal best until that date, before it starts to deteriorate, the second means eating after this date might make you unwell.

There are also numerous apps on the market that let you keep track of food you have purchased while tracking its expiry dates - some also find recipes to use what foods you have left over before they date out. Find them, use them.

The average US household spends $6600 a year on food - not wastefully throwing away a third of that could save them $2200.

Impact: Removes the need for up to one in every three bags of food we purchase.
Difficulty: Moderately hard.
Money-saving: Yes £1000+
Action: Learn about sell by dates. Plan meals. Use food apps.

I Do This Already ★ **I Choose This Task** ☐

Sort Your Soap
Cut Back on Bathroom Bottles

You may be happy to learn that the UK city of Newcastle, a place where none of the major soaps on British TV are based, was instrumental in the creation of the modern TV soap opera. You see, Newcastle was the home of a gentleman called Thomas Hedley, whose soap and candle making company created a laundry soap called Oxydol in 1914. This product became popular in the USA and Canada, and ended up being bought by Procter & Gamble of Cincinnati, Ohio in 1927.

Soaps and detergents were very profitable, and the owners of Oxydol were happy to use their money to market their laundry soap to their mostly female customers. One way they did this was to sponsor a radio drama in the 1930s called *The Ma Perkins Radio Show*. It wasn't long before this, and other radio dramas, got the name 'soap operas'. The soap being the sponsor, the opera being the style of over the top drama. If you're familiar with actual opera, you will note the similarity of overblown real-life-ish family drama, full of passion, jealously, intrigue, threats, humour, cliffhangers, murder, and plot changes aplenty. In Mozart's *The Marriage of Figaro*, a four-part opera from 1786, there is a plot line that would be the most soapy soap moment ever - when Figaro, who is being forced to marry an older woman Marcellina, discovers she is actually his own mother! Even JR Ewing, Dirty Den, Alexis Colby and Erica Kane would be shocked at that one. Whatever the later medium, via TV or streaming, soap opera had landed and is here forever.

Importantly, the reason actual soap products were profitable enough to fund radio and TV soap operas for their early years is simple. Soap is something most people use every day and fundamental to our health and hygiene.

Actual soap, the hard bar stuff that some millennials may never have used, has been with us as long as Ancient Babylon 4800 years ago. While liquid soap, the stuff most people now know as 'soap', was first patented by William Sheppard in 1865 - but only really became popular in the 1980s.

The difference between hard soap and liquid soap is simple. The hard soap can stand alone while the liquid soap needs a container of some kind. It is this minor difference, the container, or more likely the plastic container, that is helping cause massive pollution problems worldwide.

There are future solutions, such as soap bottles made from hard soap that contain liquid soap. However, for now, we have to deal with the actual problem, and, as Friends of the Earth are keen to let the world know, only 9% of all the plastic ever made has been recycled.

One simple solution to the problem of soap sold in plastic containers is to go back to using soap bars - although they don't always come unpackaged. Studies show both soaps work just as effectively at cleaning, and there are slightly more environmental reasons to use bar soap than liquid soap (mostly to do with increased energy to make liquid soap versus extra land needed to make bar soap). For those unprepared to lose liquid soap or make their own natural soaps (or buy them), there is a part way solution.

Instead of buying dozens of liquid soap bottles each year, simply buy pouch refills and fill the bottles you already own. Bulk buy pouches of 1 litre soaps are each enough to fill four 250ml bottles. This saves 85% of the plastic needed and gives an average money saving of 25%. If you want to remove that final 15% of plastic then don't buy any container and shop at one of the myriad of 'packaging free' refill stores popping up around the world.

Impact: Removes up to 85% of the plastic used in liquid soaps.
Difficulty: Super easy.
Money-saving: Yes £10+
Action: Buy refillable soap pouches rather than new plastic bottles or use refill shops.

I Do This Already  **I Choose This Task**

Use the Heat Beneath Your Feet
Go Geothermal

The most watched international sporting event on the planet was the London 2012 Summer Olympics, with a global audience of 3.6 billion people - or 50.52% of everyone on planet Earth at that time. This memorable event, with its opening ceremony depicting James Bond and Queen Elizabeth II parachuting into the Olympic stadium was a delight and one of the great moments in the history of the modern games.

The first ever Olympics is believed to have been held 2788 years earlier in Olympia, Greece in 776BC. These ancient games had participants travelling from every part of the Greek world at the time to compete - and all athletes were allowed free passage to the games as all wars were put on truce. How civilised!

The mention of the Olympics is because they came from Greece, a land that also gave the world democracy, theatre, philosophy, geometry, modern mathematics, zoology, court juries, western medicine, even showers.

Another thing the Greeks gave us (don't you simply love how sharing they are?) was their language. This is why we have words like planet (meaning to wander), dinosaur (translating as terrible lizard), music (meaning art of the muses - the greek goddesses), galaxy (translating as milk - like Milky Way), and telephone (translating as far away sound).

The Greeks also gave us the word 'geothermal' - *geo* meaning 'Earth' and *therme* meaning heat. And this word could end up being the gold medalist of the Environment Olympics, should such an event ever be held. You see, we are literally standing on top of one of the simplest, most constant, and inexpensive forms of heating imaginable - the Earth itself.

There are three types of geothermal energy. The first, 'district heating', is when heat from inside the Earth comes close to the surface as superhot water, or to the surface as natural hot springs or geysers, is then tapped into, and used to heat properties. In Iceland, for example, around 87% of all buildings are heated this way. The second, 'geothermal power', taps into the same superhot reservoirs under the Earth's surface and uses them to generate electricity. These first two types are easier to run in areas where, geologically, there is a rift in continental plates and there is volcanic activity.

The third type of geothermal energy is known as 'heat pump', and this can make a massive energy difference to millions of households around the world. Pipes are simply laid beneath the ground around a home and, through the use of a heat pump, the natural heat of the ground is transferred to radiators or underfloor heating in the property. This third system also has the benefit of being able to transfer heat back the other way (back into the ground) so can take excess heat from a house on hot days to cool the home down, much like a refrigerator works. This gives heat and air-con in one!

Once installed, heat pumps in home settings average a 75% reduction in heating costs - and a minimum 75% saving in the previous fossil fuel used. The 25% used is to power the heatpump so could come from solar panels.

New legislation in numerous countries to reduce climate change means many oil and gas boilers will soon be phased out - the UK, for example, is banning them in new build homes in 2025. Geothermal is a natural, totally sustainable, energy replacement just beneath our feet waiting to be used. A century ago, Iceland was a poor country reliant on peat or imported coal. Now it is one of the wealthiest countries in the world and 100% powered by renewable energy, mostly geothermal.

Impact: Removes at least 75% of all fossil fuel heating for homes.
Difficulty: Initially expensive but pays for itself within a few years.
Money-saving: Yes, after time.
Action: Talk to geothermal specialists to see how/if your home could benefit.

I Do This Already  **I Choose This Task** ☐

Take a Staycation or a Home Holiday

If you took the results offered on the first page of a popular search engine then the 'best place to visit on the planet' is South Island, New Zealand, or Bali, Indonesia, or Machu Picchu, Peru, or The Great Barrier Reef, Australia, or Comino Island, Malta, or Paris, France, or Chamarel, Mauritius, or London, or Croatia, or the Grand Canyon, or Barcelona, etc. In other words, no man, woman or machine knows the 'best place'. It is just too subjective.

We know the world's most visited country by international tourist arrivals is France, closely followed by Spain - with both countries receiving more visitors each year than they have actual populations. These are followed by the USA, China, Italy, Turkey, Mexico, Germany, UK, and Thailand.

Interestingly, the USA, the home of the mighty dollar, tops the list when it comes to the amount of money made from international tourism, taking $214.1 billion in 2019 - a figure which is only $14 billion less than the amounts of France, Spain, China, and Italy put together.

The most popular monuments are, not surprisingly, the Forbidden City in Beijing with 17 million visitors a year, then St Peters Basilica in the Vatican (11m), and Palace of Versailles (8.1m). Perhaps more surprising is that the Lincoln Memorial in Washington DC (7.8m) is ahead of Rome's Colosseum (7.6m) and Athen's Parthenon (7.2m). Even more surprising is all these are ahead of the Eiffel Tower in Paris and Taj Mahal in India (both 7m).

Regardless of where the best place is to visit, the one thing most of the world's international travellers, adventurers, and bucket-listers share is this - their little planes taking them to get there help create 2.4% of all global CO_2 emissions.

If everyone halved their fly-away holidays each year then that 2.4% CO_2 figure, which is bad enough, would drop to 1.2%. A problem halved is not a solution, but it is half of a solution - and also the start of a bigger solution.

This may sound a dire idea if you are a world travel freak, but when you realise that a typical return flight between Los Angeles and London creates the same amount of CO_2 for each passenger (3.5 tonnes) as every one of them driving a car for the next ten months, then you can see the damage that too much fossil fuel powered air travel can cause.

The idea of a staycation, a vacation where people use their home as a base, was first coined in the Myrtle Beach Sun-News in 2003, but really hit the public imagination in October 2005 when used in the Canadian TV comedy series *Corner Gas*. The lead character, Brent Butt, going 40 yards from home, pretending he was in Aruba, and enjoying a well-earned 'staycation'.

Whether taking a 'staycation', 'near-cation', 'home holiday' or 'domestic holiday', the basic idea is that you are not travelling overseas, and not flying. The ideal is to use your own home as a base for accommodation, or that of friends and family, and take short trips to interesting attractions in your own country/area/county/state as if you were on a normal vacation. Initially, the idea of staycations was about money saving, but for environment and then pandemic reasons this type of holiday has now become increasingly popular.

Most people don't know their own areas or countries as well as they think. Germans, for example, take more overseas tourist trips each year (90m) than they have people (83m), yet their own country is so full of attractions to foreigners (think Berlin, Bavaria, the Rhine, Black Forest, North Sea islands, etc) that it is the 8th most popular destination on Earth.

Impact: Potential to reduce up to 1.4% of all global CO_2 emissions.
Difficulty: Easy, and less hassle.
Money-saving: Yes £500+
Action: Enjoy what your own region or area has to offer.

I Do This Already  **I Choose This Task** ☐

Learn to Recycle Properly and Make Waste Become Something Good

If you ask people who live an interesting life 'What are the important things you wish you knew when you were younger?' you will get many answers. These could be from the super wise 'never hesitate when you should act', 'don't take anything for granted' or 'make every moment count' to the really odd such as 'no matter how good the smell of their soap, never walk out of a restaurant toilet sniffing your fingers', 'never marry a tennis player' ('love' means nothing to them), or 'never pee on an electric fence' (ouch!).

One piece of very sage advice you should receive is how important difference and diversity can be. Yes, we may all love mountains but sometimes we need a desert or an ocean to put that love into perspective. Pepper goes best with salt, not more pepper. Sugar goes well with spice, not more sugar. It seems all our yins go better when they find their yangs. We may live for one particular thing but, as legendary football manager Pep Guardiola discovered when he famously sought ideas from the games of water polo and chess, you can improve whatever you do by looking at different things.

Difference is important, really important, and understanding two things about the differences in recycling will help the environment. The first is that everywhere has a different recycling system, the second is, although everything can theoretically be recycled, what you think may be recyclable, may be very different from what your recycling centre will actually recycle.

Before you even try to recycle, it might be worth noting that, even in places with super high recycling rates, like the UK, at least **one in ten** items carefully put in the recycling bin end up in 'waste-to-energy' incinerators.

If people want to recycle well, then we must be prepared for the frustration of different products being recyclable in one place but not another.

Each waste and recycling service in the world is different. South Ayrshire in Scotland use five wheelie bins and one caddy, Cheshire East in England use three wheelie bins, while the next county along, Shropshire, use two wheelie bins, two open plastic boxes, one caddy and blue bags. Heidelberg in Germany uses two wheelie bins and yellow bags. Chicago uses two wheelie bins, while Austin, Texas, has two wheelie bins and yard bags. All are different sizes and, sadly, there is no universal colour for each type of recycling - aluminium cans go in silver in Cheshire East, blue in Chicago, yellow in Germany and black in Shropshire.

Confusion aside, the reality is that people should work with the local system they have as best they can. All waste and recycling services will supply a list of what can go in each kerbside wheelie bin, cart, box, bag, caddy, etc. and what items, if any, can be picked up individually. There is normally a recycling centre of some kind in each area where you can take different items.

Good recycling means clean recycling - dirty or half empty yoghurt cartons in plastic recycling, or plastic in paper only collections, will just contaminate the full load and everything will end up in landfill or 'waste to energy' incinerators.

Don't forget the small stuff! It is also useful to create an area in your home (such as the garage) where you can store small items for recycling. Batteries can go in a sealed jar, old bulbs in a box, cooking oils in a container, etc., until full enough to be worthy of a trip to the recycling centre.

Recycling is important. If old baked bean tins could dream, they would do so about being recycled properly and returning as something really cool, like part of a skyscraper or Tesla. Help that dream ... recycle well, recycle clean.

Impact: Potential to increase correct recycling rates by 10%.
Difficulty: Moderately easy.
Money-saving: No.
Action: Read the rules for recycling in your local area. Keep all recycling items clean.

I Do This Already  **I Choose This Task** ☐

Remove Impulse Purchases Go Kerbside and Click and Collect

If we offer clues, can you guess the ***Englishman In New York***? He felt ***So Lonely*** about the environment he wrote a ***Message In A Bottle*** to voice his worries about ***Every Breath You Take***. He said ***Don't Stand So Close To Me*** to polluters as he told ***Roxanne***, a recycler, that ***Every Little Thing She Does Is Magic***. He knew his planet was dying, didn't want to feel like he was ***Walking On the Moon*** so proclaimed ***I Can't Stand Losing You***.

If you've not already guessed, the person is Gordon Sumner, the son of a milkman father and a hairdresser mother, born in 1951 on the outskirts of Newcastle in England, and better known to the world as the singer Sting.

The reason this very talented gentleman is being mentioned is that he plays a significant role in history - one that is becoming bigger every passing year - and one that will likely have him spoken about in the future in the same way as historians today talk about Neil Armstrong, Johannes Gutenberg, Alexander Graham Bell, or Robert Stephenson. You see, his CD album *Ten Summoner's Tales* was, on 11 August 1994, the first ever item bought via a completely new medium - online shopping.

The seller of the item was Dan Kohn of Philadelphia who had the idea of online commerce while attending the London School of Economics as a student at Swarthmore College in Pennsylvania. He made his sale via his website 'NetMarket' to Phil Brandenberger, a close friend of his from Philadelphia. The $12.48 price being paid by encrypted credit card.

Now serving over one in five retail sales globally, the increasingly welcoming shop door to the world of online shopping had opened.

Online shopping is very much a part of our planet, with at least one estimate suggesting 2.1 billion people on Earth have purchased items this way. Most sales are straight online orders and items are delivered the next day, or a few days later - or even minutes later in some locations.

With regard to the environment, online shopping means two very important things. The first is that we can purchase items from suppliers we trust and like, have fair prices, and good 'environment first' policies and practices. The second is that for things like supermarket shopping we can use the 'click and collect' or 'kerbside pick-up' system very much to our advantage.

Most global research shows that when people go in-store they will spend more money (at least 15% more in one report) than if they had simply ordered their shopping online and used the 'click and collect' option.

It seems, psychologically at least, that not physically entering a den of retail allows you to evade most of the promotions, offers, free samples, and other temptations. We are mere humans, we buy emotionally, we purposely do 'retail therapy', and our eyes (and their shopping carts) are bigger than our stomachs. Then add that some retail organisations are even bigger than countries. Walmart, for example, has 10,526 stores and its 2.3 million employees number more than the whole US military (2.23 million).

You are one person, they have armies of marketeers and ad guys whose sole purpose is to make you want their things. Every product also has people working to make you buy. You are putty in their hands.

The planet, and your wallet, need you to spend 15% less every week on shopping. Remove impulse purchases and go click and collect - or better still, go to a simple refill shop and evade all promo packaging and retail BS.

Impact: Can reduce excess shopping by up to 15%.
Difficulty: Easy, and time saving.
Money-saving: Yes £500+
Action: Use shops for specialist things, online for very specialist things, and click and collect for store shopping.

I Choose This Task

Never Bathe Alone

If you ever wondered where Daniel Radcliffe was when he found out he had been given the role of Harry Potter then you will be happy to know he was in the bath. Ancient Greek scholar Archimedes ended up running naked down the streets of Syracuse screaming 'Eureka' (I've found it) after discovering how to measure the volume of objects by noticing the water displacement as he stepped into his full bath. Singer Freddie Mercury wrote the Queen hit, 'Crazy Little Thing Called Love' while in a bath in a Munich hotel. The United States almost doubled in size after French leader Napoleon Bonaparte decided to sell the Louisiana Territory to the USA while in his bath.

Big things can, and do, happen in the bath! But even better things can happen if you take a bath but don't bathe alone.

The earliest sanitation system and first known bathing areas date from the Indus Valley Civilisation found in modern day Pakistan and parts of India and Afghanistan around 5,000 years ago. However, the first known bathtub dates from 3500 years ago and is found at the Palace of Knossos in Crete.

The bathtub throughout history, in varying shapes and sizes around the world, was mostly made from wood. This began to change in the 1800s when portable copper or tin tubs, filled once and then shared by all the family, became popular. In the 1880s Scottish born American inventor David Dunbar Buick created a way to bond porcelain enamel to cast iron and what we would know as the traditional house bath was born - later changing to fibreglass, then acrylic materials in the 1960s and 1970s.

Incidentally, Buick used his enamel bath money to set up the Buick Motor Company, today part of General Motors, and his name has been seen on over 45 million cars.

We love our baths and sometimes go to extreme lengths to make them as luxurious/weird as possible. Egyptian leader Cleopatra reputedly bathed in asses milk (which took the milk of 23 asses), while Hungarian Countess Elizabeth Bathory, is reputed to have bathed in the blood of female virgins.

In more modern history, in 2012, the famous Cadogan Hotel in London offered a 'Champagne Bath' as part of its hotel services. This consisted of 120 bottles of Dom Perignon 2002 (warmed or cooled to a temperature the guests desired) and cost, at the time, a whopping £25,000.

The Japanese are among the greatest bathers in the world with most surveys suggesting over two-thirds of Japanese have a bath every day - some even taking showers before their bath. In Europe, the 'bathiest' nation is the UK, which, although more a shower nation these days, still manages to have two-fifths of its population take a bath at least once a week. In Germany around one-fifth of the population have a bath at least once a week, while that figure is barely over one in nine in the USA.

The nation thought to be the most bath loving on the planet is Malawi where it is not uncommon for people to bathe up to three times a day. However many of these baths are taken in the form of a stand in basin/bucket bath.

But why should we never bathe alone? From an environmental stance, the average bath uses 132 litres of water, so we half that to save 66 litres each when we share a bath. Also, two people taking an average 8 minute shower, each using 12 litres of water per minute would use 192 litres.

From a safety perspective, using Japan as the example, at least 10% of the 14,000 people who die in the bath there each year (three times more than die in car accidents) would not have died if they had someone with them.

Impact: Weekly bathing with someone saves 6,864 litres of water a year.
Difficulty: Easy, but tap end less so.
Money-saving: Yes £10+
Action: Run a bath. Find a friend.

I Choose This Task ☐

If You Need to Fly Fly Economy

On the 6th May, 1937, the LZ 129 Hindenburg had just flown across the Atlantic Ocean to the USA on its journey from Frankfurt in Germany. The Hindenburg was the world's largest airship, almost as large as the Empire State Building placed on its side. It stayed aloft by use of hydrogen gas, while its 4 Daimler engines allowed a maximum speed of 85 mph (135 kph). It had a crew of 61 and space for over 50 passengers, each paying $450, the equivalent of $7500 today, to have a cabin with a bed, and access to a large, opulent dining room, reading room, even a smoking room and bar.

Sadly, as the airship was attempting to moor up at Lakehurst Airfield in New Jersey it caught fire and exploded. Within seconds 13 passengers, 22 crewmen, and 1 ground staff worker had died or would later die in hospital. The spectacular explosion became global news and effectively ended the reign of the airship as a safe and efficient means of travel.

Amazingly, almost nine decades later, a larger 'aircraft' has yet to be built and, at a length of 245m (803ft), the Hindenburg was well over three times the length and three times the height of the largest commercial airliner in the world today - the Airbus A380.

The Airbus A380, nicknamed the 'SuperJumbo', has a floorspace measuring 550 square metres on its two decks. Most airlines that use the aircraft do so with a seating configuration that allows around 470 passengers.

We, therefore, now live in a world where an aircraft which is over nine times smaller than the largest airship ever, can carry nine times more passengers. The most interesting thing for the environment is this same aircraft is certified to carry up to 383 more people if they chose to remove first and business class - and just offered economy seats.

It is estimated that the aviation industry creates around 2.4% of all global CO2 emissions. Naturally, it would be better if that figure was zero, but in the real world we need fast and efficient modes of long distance travel. Until we have all-electric planes (and they already exist and are in the process of being scaled up) then we need quick solutions today.

Changing the inside of the largest aircraft in the world to seat 81% more passengers would mean, in practical terms, that we would need far fewer long distance flights and therefore create far less CO2 emissions. A neat and simple solution, but one that is unlikely to be used as airlines generally make 75% of their profits on each flight from the First and Business class sections of their planes.

If people really must fly, one way in which the individual can make a difference to the environment is simply to ignore the expensive seats and go economy. Passengers may be slightly more cramped but they can at least console themselves in the knowledge they are not spending the typical four times the amount of money just to be up at the front of the aircraft. They will also know that they are personally creating three times less carbon emissions than first class passengers even though they are on the same flight (think extra space and lots of heavier stuff, bigger seats, more equipment, more food, more staff, and lots more champagne, etc.).

Everyone loves a bit of luxury and opulence now and then - but where we choose to be luxurious really matters if the main concern is the environment - and being unnecessarily grand and fancy in mid-air is not the place.

It is far better to take three important flights in economy than one pointless First Class flight with champagne and caviar.

Impact: Helps aircraft transport more people without increasing emissions.
Difficulty: Easy.
Money-saving: Yes £1000+
Action: Where you would normally book First/Business Class, book economy.

I Do This Already  **I Choose This Task** ☐

Don't Ignore, Don't Panic, and Don't Believe the Hype

Thanks to comedy genius Douglas Adams, if people are asked the question: 'What is the meaning of life, the universe, and everything?', they will likely answer with: '42'. Even Google and Bing will answer with '42' (try it!).

Now here's the thing, even though people say '42', the reality is that in Douglas Adams books, radio series, TV series and film of *The Hitchhikers Guide To The Galaxy*, the actual answer to 'What is the meaning of life, the universe, and everything?' was never discovered. The number 42 was an answer that took 7.5 million years to work out by a computer called Deep Thought, but that same computer also pointed out that the answer was flawed because the question itself was flawed. Another computer would be needed (in the shape of the planet Earth) and would take 10 million years to work out just the question itself. Only then could an answer be sought.

Totally different subject, but among the many surveys of best US President in history there are certain names that are always among the top ten. One of those names is Ronald Reagan, the actor turned politician credited with ending the Cold War with the Soviet Union. He is so highly regarded, his Presidential Library is the most visited in the USA. Sadly, Reagan is also the man who persuaded people in 1940s advertisements that Chesterfield cigarettes were his favourite and that they were 'mild'. In real life he never actually smoked cigarettes - and those 'mild' cigarettes still killed people.

The two things are mentioned to show that sometimes, like '42', we prefer the lie to the facts, and sometimes, like Reagan, even our heroes are used by others to persuade us to think, do, or go in one direction or another.

Facts and lies, said by saints and sinners. When it comes to the environment so much is said by so many people that it is easy to feel petrified about our future on one side and so blissfully ignorant on another.

The skill to differentiate between a peer-reviewed fact and a dangerous PR slanted story on behalf of fearful or predatory businesses working for their bottom line is important. Similarly, it is vital to understand the difference between a fact and a shamelessly pessimistic PR story on behalf of overly biased environmentalists trying to push or fund a specific agenda.

Regardless of whatever a celebrity gets paid to tell you: No, you do not need to plant a tree for every mile you drive to make up for carbon emissions. No, the planet will not end because you don't make your own toothpaste or urinate on a compost heap. No, you don't have to become anti-baby for fear they will use all future resources. No, your hybrid car is not carbon neutral. No, that sweater made from plastic cups is not a solution for plastic pollution. No, that so-called 'clean gas' is anything but clean.

Don't be suckered, one way or another. Ignore the ads. There is only one of you, and you might be very smart, but whatever you've got, they have a whole marketing team - and a way bigger budget than you'll ever have to counter them with. They also have the power to take the people you like, such as film stars, sports stars, even real life heroes - and pay them to say things are good - that may not actually be good for you, your family, or the planet.

As Eighties hip-hop group Public Enemy famously once sang 'Don't Believe The Hype'. If we add this to Douglas Adams 'Don't panic!' and this book's 'Don't ignore!' message then the fight for the environment will get just facts - and only actual knowledge can guide what real actions we need to do.

Impact: Only real information and facts help us solve environment problems.
Difficulty: Very hard.
Money-saving: No.
Action: Only take information from trusted peer-reviewed sources.

I Choose This Task

Buy Just Two Items of Clothing Each Season

The late Steve Jobs has had four feature films made about his life, with four famous Hollywood actors - Michael Fassbender, Ashton Kutcher, Justin Long and Noah Wyle - each playing the role of the billionaire Apple co-founder.

The costume departments of each film must have been so upset, but the film's accountants so happy, that the main character was almost the easiest person ever to clothe - down to one simple fact - for much of his life Steve Jobs wore the same outfit every day, a simple black turtleneck designed by Issey Miyake, a pair of Levi's jeans, and silvery grey New Balance trainers. Jobs was, in clothing terms, the polar opposite of Liberace, Elton John, Kanye West, David Bowie, Freddie Mercury, and Elvis Presley.

Steve Jobs wasn't scruffy, unclean or a penny pincher. He had several copies of each item of clothing. He was simply averse to something called 'decision fatigue', an emotional and mental strain that most people experience when faced with too many decisions. Essentially, Jobs, was trying to keep his mind as fresh as possible by removing dozens of unnecessary daily decisions - and he didn't want the hassle of trying to work out each day what clothes he should wear. He was also conscious of his own personal brand.

This same behaviour is seen in many other people including Barack Obama (same blue or grey suits), Mark Zuckerberg (grey t-shirt with black or navy hoodie), Albert Einstein (grey suit), Hillary Clinton (pantsuits), and when not wearing a spacesuit, Sir Richard Branson (jeans and white shirt).

Minimalist clothing, it appears, helps people make better decisions - saves money - saves time - and helps people become their own personal brand.

Minimalist clothing also helps the environment, and the notion that less is more is very appealing when you consider that in nations such as the United States the average American buys at least one item of clothing every week.

The global resources squandered to keep this 'fast fashion' rolling have doubled every twenty years over the past four decades - a rate the planet simply cannot accommodate. The once massive Aral Sea (which was the size of the Republic of Ireland in 1960) was over used by Soviet Union planners to supply water to irrigate cotton fields in the area that is now in Kazakhstan and Uzbekistan and is now almost completely gone. A once plentiful inland sea, this now barren wasteland has been renamed the Aralkum Desert.

If we took an average American, then the 50 plus items of clothing they buy each year would use up to the equivalent in just water alone of 12 typical Florida in-ground home swimming pools measuring 24ft by 12ft by 5ft deep. And that's just one person in one year. Even more startling on a global level, is that the clothing industry around the world has a carbon footprint almost equal to that of all member nations of the European Union combined.

One solution to this madness is to go minimalist and buy only 2 items of new clothing each season - excluding underwear and second hand clothes.

Buying a maximum of 8 items of new clothing each year puts more thought into what is purchased. More durable, less easily worn-out, de-coloured, stretched, and shrinkable clothing becomes the norm. Momentary ad-guided fashion gets replaced by individualism, long wearing guarantees make a come-back, and people are more inclined to make sure clothes fit perfectly (which is one big reason for wasted clothes in the first place).

Save the next Aral Sea from becoming a desert - buy only two items of new clothing each season.

Impact: Reduce global environment impact of fashion by up to one-third.
Difficulty: Hard.
Money-saving: Yes £200+
Action: Simply limit yourself to two items of new clothing each season.

I Choose This Task

Why Buy a Battery When You Can Recharge?

The earliest known sculptured depiction of a human face was created around 5100 years ago and found in 1939 by archaeologists at Uruk in present day Iraq. Made of white marble, this beautiful female face was given the name 'the Mask of Warka' and housed in the National Museum of Iraq in Baghdad.

In 2003 during the first weeks of the Invasion of Iraq by a US led coalition, the mask, along with 15,000 other priceless antiquities, disappeared in the looting and mayhem of war. One other item to disappear was a two millennia old artefact known as the 'Baghdad Battery', a ceramic pot with copper tube and iron rod that was theorised to be the world's first battery.

The Mask of Uruk was later returned to the Museum (it was found on a farm in northern Iraq) but the Baghdad Battery has simply vanished - only adding to the supposed mystery that ancients were somehow technologically aware.

In reality, from what we know already about the Baghdad Battery the evidence is that, yes, it could have been used as a battery, indeed there have been several experiments showing how it would work. However, it would be incredibly inefficient and the ancients might have been better using a lemon or dozens of other items as a rudimentary battery.

The world would have to wait another 1800 plus years for the first true battery to be invented by Italian scientist Alessandro Volta (1799). In the 22 decades since, batteries have transformed our world (think torches, portable radios, moon missions, calculators, laptops, etc.) and with the advent of gigafactories and increasing knowledge about how to store energy into ever more smaller spaces, it looks like our world may be about to change again.

The world, collectively, once they have finished using their household AA, AAA, AAAA, C, D, 9V, CR123A, 23A batteries, powering things like remote controls, toys, calculators, smoke alarms, etc, will throw away over 15 billion of the things every year.

Most disposable household batteries comprise 25% steel and 15% paper and/or plastic - the remaining 60% is made from a combination of zinc, manganese, potassium, and graphite. Globally, the vast majority will end up in landfill. Even in places like the European Union, where there are strict regulations on battery disposal and numerous places to return used batteries, only 47% will end up being recycled.

The strange thing about household batteries is that the disposable ones are vastly more popular than the rechargeable ones. This seems to be down to a purchasing habit from which people can't break free.

Dependent on where a person lives, most disposable batteries are around seven to ten times cheaper than rechargeable batteries. Strangely, even though numerous studies have consistently shown that good rechargeable batteries can be successfully recharged over 500 times, the majority of consumers happily ignore the fact they can get hundreds of battery uses for minimal top-up costs compared to a single one-use only disposable battery.

Most people would never think of putting a new battery in their mobile phone every time it ran out of power - yet that is exactly what we do with normal household batteries.

Time to save your money, buy top quality rechargeable batteries, and save the need for at least 499 other disposable batteries ever having to be manufactured, packaged, transported, sold, then recycled or dumped.

Impact: Removes need for over 500 disposable batteries.
Difficulty: Easy.
Money-saving: Yes £50+
Action: Buy, and use, battery charger and rechargeable batteries.

I Choose This Task ☐

Use Rewashable Bags and Boxes Instead of Plastic Shopping Bags

Did you know that the average American has four credit cards - access to $31,000 in credit on them, and an average credit card debt of $6,000?

Did you also know that the average credit card weighs 5 grams or that the average person on planet Earth will eat the equivalent of one credit card in plastics - every week?

A study at the University of Newcastle in New South Wales, Australia, commissioned by the World Wildlife Fund, on the amount of plastic ingested by humans, recently discovered that the average person will consume about 2000 tiny pieces of plastic, called microplastics, every year. These add up to around 5 grams a week (or the equivalent of eating one credit card).

The greatest ingestion of this plastic was through water, where double the amount was found in the USA and India than in Europe. Microplastics were also ingested from shellfish, fish, beer, honey, salt and sugar. The last two are the biggest shock because salt or sugar are found in almost every food on the planet. Micro plastics are literally everywhere yet plastic wasn't even invented in a form we would understand until little over a century ago, in 1907, when Belgian-American Leo Baekeland created Bakelite.

The world is plastic crazy. It has even been suggested that our love for plastic and the way we overuse it is similar to the Ancient Greek mythology of King Midas. This King, when being given the gift of turning everything he touched into gold, was soon in despair when he found that whatever he tried to eat or drink became gold. He was rich, but gold is not a food. Even worse, while comforting his daughter, Marigold, she too became gold.

In the story of King Midas there was a happy ending, everything could return to normal if the King washed himself in the River Pactolus. His daughter Marigold also came back to life and all was well.

In our real, not mythical world, our Midas touch is not gold, but plastic, and it has come back to bite us even harder than gold ever did to King Midas.

One of the Midas touches that has caused major global problems is the advent of the plastic shopping bag. The Earth Day organisers suggest that one trillion single-use plastic bags are used across the planet every year - that would mean 1.9 million are used every minute of every day. Sadly, these plastic bags do not all end up in some wonderful re-use, re-use, recycle, re-use, re-use, recycle, never-ending happy loop. It is estimated that worldwide only 12% will be recycled, while the rest will end up as landfill, incinerated, or find their way into our rivers and oceans.

The simplest way to stop this problem is to simply stop or reduce single-use plastic bags altogether. A 5p levy on once free supermarket plastic bags in England in 2015 saw a reduction in use of over 97%. In 2014, the year before the levy, supermarket customers used an average of 140 a year each. Today that figure is less than four.

Good replacements for plastic bags are boxes made from recycled plastic or wood that can be used thousands of times, more durable multi-use bags, or best of all, a set of simple cotton bags - the type that can be folded very small but are strong enough to carry lots of shopping. Washable is best, especially as over use of any bag or box can lead to bacteria and mould growth. Colourful is also good so you can use different coloured bags for different foods such as meats or vegetables to reduce possible cross-contamination.

Impact: Removes up to 97% of plastic bags from becoming microplastics, landfill or fumes.
Difficulty: Very easy.
Money-saving: Yes £5+
Action: Take cotton bags or boxes with you when shopping.

I Choose This Task

Are You the Problem? Do You Work For the Bad Guys?

It is doubtful you have ever heard of Stanislav Petrov, but if he had never existed then it is most likely you would also never have existed, or, if born before 26 September 1983, that would have been the date of your death.

Petrov was a lieutenant colonel in the Soviet Air Defence Force on that date. On duty for the nightshift at a command centre for the Soviet Union's nuclear attack early warning system. In the early hours he received confirmation on his computers of a missile attack from the United States. The information in front of him was clear. It had passed 29 layers of security protocols before getting to him. His duty was also clear. He had to make one simple phone call which would begin the process of a retaliatory strike by the full arsenal of nuclear missiles against the United States and its NATO allies.

Petrov's unit had trained many times for this scenario and he understood that time wasted now could affect the ability of the Soviet Union to retaliate. Petrov had no option but to make that call, the call that would end the world as we knew it - but he had a nagging doubt. The order of the US missile launches was sporadic, not a massed attack - and even though he was trained to base his judgment call solely on the information on his computers, his radar operators were not detecting any missiles. Was this a ruse? New radar-busting missiles? He didn't know; but couldn't hesitate.

He made the call - deciding 'system error - no launch' then waited the worst few minutes of his life to see if he was correct - or dead. No missiles landed.

We live today because when push came to shove Petrov chose humanity and sense over rigid orders. The world needs more people like him.

In the history of humanity, the 1983 nuclear false alarm was the closest we ever came to total global annihilation. Sadly, as the climergency unfolds before our eyes, we are facing a similar humanity destroying event - just at a much slower timescale than the few heart-stopping seconds offered to Stanislav Petrov. Even so, we need to make important decisions now. Each of us needs to work out personally whether we are: Fighting to overcome the problem. Meekly accepting our fate. Actively making the problem worse.

We don't just need to look at our lifestyle, eating habits, energy use, etc. Could it be our job that's actually one of the things destroying the environment?

People may not be directly dumping chemicals into rivers, putting palm oil in foods that don't need it, running a coal power station, chopping down rainforest, working on 'gain of function' virus research, operating the digger that removes a village, or tarmacking every field we see. No, most of us are too clean for this type of thing. But we may be inadvertently assisting such activities through our day to day jobs, helping perpetuate the nightmare for everyone else.

We see some of the most creative minds on the planet using their skills to create ads for fast fashion brands or glossily manage PR for companies who actively break environmental regulations. Architects designing battery farms and fracking rigs. Lawyers defending dodgy companies and corrupt individuals, and sales people pushing products they know are useless.

Much better, and more honourable, is to redirect our skills to fighting climate change. An architect designing green homes and infrastructure, PR guys promoting renewable energy, lawyers fighting polluters, security staff protecting wildlife, sales people selling eco holidays.

The real career skill is to know how to repurpose our talents in a direction that does most good.

Impact: Any role that directly or indirectly helps the planet is good.
Difficulty: Very hard, but so rewarding.
Money-saving: Yes-No-Maybe.
Action: Repurpose individual skills and talents for benefit of the environment.

I Choose This Task ☐

Try Not To Use Single-Use Plastics

Could you imagine the largest weighing machine ever created in the universe? A machine so great it could take the entire population of a planet and accurately weigh everyone in one go - in whatever measure you wanted, pounds, stones, kilograms, tons, ounces, even drams, grams or grains. It might not fit on a bathroom floor but this galactic weighing machine would be awesome - and called something like Star Weighs (for measuring things that are far-far-a-weigh!).

If such a machine existed it would take all 7.9 billion of us on Earth - each human having a globally average weight of 62 kilograms (136.7 pounds) - and come to a combined weight of 489,800,000,000 kilograms or 1,079,824,160,182 pounds.

This is an amazing super-heavy weight, one that even Atlas, the mythological Ancient Greek god, might have a problem lifting. It is also the same weight as the amount of plastic our world will throw away every 18 months.

Yes, you heard correctly, the average human will throw away the equivalent of their body weight in plastic every 18 months.

Our species is truly trashy.

Most of this waste will come in the form of single-use plastics - those occasionally super useful, but normally unnecessary, bits of plastic that make up things like cigarette butts, drink bottles, food wrapping, grocery bags, straws, caps, plastic cutlery, packaging, etc.

This type of plastic, made from chemicals created from oil, is purposely designed to be used once and then recycled, but we can see on any street, river, and beach, that this is not happening.

Worldwide, not even 12% is recycled, and this plastic causes big problems further down the line for the planet, nature, climate, and human health.

The 88% of waste plastic that is not recycled will either be incinerated, put in landfills nearby, exported to landfills in poorer countries, find its way into unregulated trash mountains, or end up … well, anywhere and everywhere.

Thankfully, there has been some governmental efforts to reduce the sale of single-use plastics. The UK, for example, banned the supply of plastic straws, stirrers, and cotton buds in 2020, while Kenya banned them in 2017. Many other countries, such as China and Canada, as well as the European Union, have dates to ban single-use plastics, while others have 'pledged' to do so before 2030 (this last one is called 'kicking the can down the road').

It is painfully obvious that humanity cannot rely entirely on governments to stop the single-use plastics crisis, and we need to make personal steps to change the situation.

The simple thing to make a change is to find alternatives to the plastic versions. Instead of buying one of the 1.9 million plastic grocery bags that are used across the planet every minute of the day, use something like long-lasting natural baskets, boxes, or cloth bags to carry shopping. Instead of using plastic stirrers or cutlery, use wooden versions, or better still actual cutlery. Instead of using plastic straws, use paper ones, or better still, long lasting metal ones, or no straw at all. Instead of using plastic stick cotton buds/swabs, use the ones made of rolled paper, wood or bamboo. Instead of buying takeaway food or drink in a polystyrene container, buy from a place that uses card, or better still, has a returnable container system, or even better, let's you use your own plate or mug.

Plastics are vital for many uses, but where they create bigger problems than they solve, we must strive to use alternatives.

Impact: Reduces your body weight in plastic pollution every 18 months.
Difficulty: Moderately easy.
Money-saving: Yes £10+
Action: Stop using single-use plastics wherever possible. Use alternatives.

I Choose This Task

Use Plants to Remove Street Pollution and Insulate Your Home

Saturday 26 April 1986 was a very big day for Arnold Alois Schwarzenegger. The Hollywood A-Lister and later Governor of California, was starring in one of the biggest roles of his life - his wedding to Maria Shriver, part of the famous Kennedy clan. Former US First Lady Jackie Kennedy Onassis attended, as did Andy Warhol, Andy Williams, Grace Jones, and Oprah Winfrey.

As the guests gathered for the ceremony, some 4,444 miles away in a place called Pripyat in the Soviet Union, a different group were gathering. Nuclear scientists, all frantically trying to work out how to deal with an explosion in the number 4 reactor at the Chernobyl Nuclear Power Plant.

We know the story. This became the single worst nuclear disaster in history and did in a few days more damage than Schwarzenegger's most famous destructive character, The Terminator, could ever have done. Within hours the whole city of Pripyat was hastily evacuated - its residents never to return - and as events unfolded, over one third of a million people in the area would end up being resettled in other parts of the Soviet Union.

It is estimated that up to 60 tonnes of radioactive material escaped into the atmosphere and radiation was spread as far as Ireland. The official death toll from the disaster was 31 but, it is estimated that many thousands more died (and will die) in the following months and years from radiation exposure.

The 20 miles exclusion zone placed around Chernobyl still exists (war permitting), and Pripyat is the ultimate urban ghost town with row after row of now greening apartment blocks and streets. It is suggested that the area will not be safe for humans to return permanently for the next 20,000 years.

The reason for the mention of Chernobyl is that in the aftermath of the disaster, in an effort to reduce the radioactive metals in the area, thousands of sunflowers were planted. This was not some Van Gogh inspired style of a post-nuclear art project. It had a serious purpose. The sunflowers have this great ability to extract radioactive metals from the ground and from water. The sunflowers, once grown, were then removed, and after being forced to decompose through a process called pyrolysis, the radioactive metals left behind were placed in solid glass and stored deep underground.

In the aftermath of the Fukushima nuclear accident in Japan in March 2011, sunflowers were used again, as were other plants, such as Indian mustard. These types of plants are known as hyperaccumulators and through a process called phytomediation, these, and other plants, can be used to remove all kinds of wastes from the ground and the atmosphere.

Plants can help us overcome many forms of pollution and one particularly useful plant is a bush called Cotoneaster franchetii - which literally soaks up road pollution. Just planting a two metre hedge of this plant will, when mature, soak up in the space of just one week a similar amount of pollution as a car driving 1000 miles. It is literally unfathomable why this plant, and others like it, are not at the front of every home and along every main road in every city - but they could be if people understood their value.

In a similar manner, things like ivy growing up walls on town and city houses and buildings will not only help reduce pollution, but will also help to insulate the property to which they are attached.

Use plants wisely and they will more than pay their way - they are one of the main tools in the fight against pollution and climate change.

Impact: Enough carbon eating plants could remove all global climate changing CO2 emissions.
Difficulty: Moderately easy.
Money-saving: No.
Action: Plant carbon eating plants and trees wherever possible.

I Do This Already ★ **I Choose This Task** ☐

Learn to Use Your Phone

When people overseas are asked what visitor attractions there are in the UK, the standard replies normally include Big Ben, Buckingham Palace, Stonehenge, Tower Bridge, Edinburgh Castle, the Eden Project, Loch Ness, the Natural History Museum, Mount Snowdon, Trafalgar Square, Kew Gardens, Hampton Court Palace, Chester Zoo, St Paul's Cathedral, Albert Docks, Shakespeare's Birthplace, etc.

Oddly, if any of those same people have actually been to the UK, you can almost guarantee that one thing they never mention will almost certainly be among their vacation photos - a pic of them standing by a red telephone box. Indeed, a red telephone box outside the Houses of Parliament that has a backdrop of Big Ben is one of the most photographed places on the planet.

The red telephone box, designed in 1924 by Sir Giles Gilbert Scott, is an icon of everything British and a photo magnet to every first time traveller to the UK. But ask those same people the last time they used a phone box anywhere and you can be sure the answer is 'not this century' - if ever.

The phone box is not dead, but it is mostly an underused relic from the past. It's original purpose made redundant by mobile phones. From a high of over 73,000 at the end of the 1970s there are now estimated to be just 5,000 still dotted around the UK. In the USA, there were 2.1 million payphones at the turn of the century, now there are less than 100,000. Clarke Kent must feel very restricted when trying to change into his alter ego, Superman!

Phone boxes were forced to change or become shower cubicles for the rich, and many are now repurposed for 21st century life as defibrillators, mini-libraries, coffee shops, art galleries, even workshops for phone and laptop repairs. The reason for their change, the phone in everyone's pocket, has improved all our lives. Now, it's time to use this tech to the benefit of the environment.

Our phones are no longer phones as people in 1980 would have seen a phone - as a talking device. Today's 'world in your pocket' machine would have amazed, and most likely shocked and scared people of just 40 years ago, like fire did when first seen by ancient cave dwellers.

Our phones today are 'everything books', making us instantly contactable, connected, knowledgable, and up-to-date. They are the greatest global game-changer. When Germans wanted a word for their mobile phones, they dropped the 'phone' and used the English word 'handy', because that's exactly what the mobile phone is today - the most handy tool ever created.

The average person in the modern world will spend three and a half hours on their 'smart' phones each day, and what people do with that time can have a direct impact on the environment.

Understanding the apps available on your phone is vital. Even the simple stuff, like using a digital organiser instead of a paper diary, taking photos of leaflets instead of actual leaflets, using maps instead of guessing a route, etc., will make a difference. There are a whole world of applications that can help you do so many environment friendly things. Good examples include: find where different things can be recycled, locate electric car power points, work out your carbon footprint, work out your waterprint, carpool, find how green certain food products are, find the chemical composition of products, link restaurants' unsold food with people on a budget, swap/sell/donate clothes and other items, upcycle products, volunteer, check ingredients, find water refill points, report fly-tipping or abandoned cars, grow food, find pollution levels in your area, and thousands of other useful things.

The tech to help the environment is in your hands. Use it, and do so wisely.

Impact: Phones share knowledge. Knowledge is the single greatest tool of change.
Difficulty: Quite easy.
Money-saving: Yes £100+
Action: Use apps on your phone to gain info and link up with other environment friendly people and organisations.

I Do This Already  **I Choose This Task**

Drive Efficiently

Formula One is a funny old sport, what else uses a 20 button steering wheel, has $300,000 diamonds embedded in the car's nose cone (Monaco 2004), has pit crew dress up as Star Wars Stormtroopers (Monaco 2005), has every driver who takes part with the surname Hill win at least one Championship (Phil 1961, Graham 1962 & 1968 and Damon 1996), has manhole covers on the track - all of which need welding down (Monaco), or have it's youngest-ever racer, Max Verstappen, be driven home from a race he just took part in because he didn't have a driving licence (Australia 2015).

Formula One is exciting, glamorous, and popular - but not really famed for reducing climate change. Yes, great strides are happening via F1 engineers with regards to fuel technology and engine efficiency. Yes, there are advances in aerodynamics and tyre design, but even so, the racing cars still use CO2 emitting fuels, and even the non-racing cars, such as the safety car or medical car are, at the time of writing, fuelled by V8 engines.

The undisputed king of the sport over the past few years has been Britain's Lewis Hamilton. And here's the thing, when Hamilton steps away from the petrol fumes of the race track he concentrates on his own personal carbon footprint - and drives electric cars.

We can all drive fast and furious - but sometimes we need to drive a little more 'Hamilton-at-Home' style, and put our planet first.

The reality is that if people want to help the planet then they should drive less - go by public transport, carpool, bike, walk - or get an electric car like Lewis Hamilton. If these options are not feasible then learn to drive the car you have more efficiently. It will reduce your impact on the planet, ensure your car lasts longer, give a better resale price, and will save you money.

Driving a fossil-fuel powered vehicle is normally the single worst thing people choose to do on a daily basis as it will only hasten the more serious effects of climate change. How we travel matters. If people are using a CO2 emitting car it is therefore important to learn to drive with the environment in mind. The first, and most obvious, tip is to know the route - a good satellite navigation system can save at least 5% in wasted fuel - or much higher on longer journeys.

If you need to drive and have two cars, take the one that's the most fuel efficient. The US Environmental Protection Agency (EPA) suggests that for someone driving 15,000 miles a year, taking the 50 Miles per Gallon (MPG) car instead of a 25 MPG car will save 20 trips to the fuel station every year - enough to pay for a years worth of weekly cinema trips and a new laptop.

Check the tyres on your car are inflated at recommended pressures as each 1% below the recommended level drops fuel efficiency by 1%. Keeping to the speed limits will improve your fuel economy by over 10% - yes, you will save one dollar in every ten by being lawful (and not get a speeding ticket). Having a regularly serviced car and holding back on quick acceleration and quick braking are important. Not driving off from traffic signals and stop signs as though you were in the Indianapolis 500 - say 0-60 in 15 seconds instead of 0-60 in 5 seconds, will improve your fuel economy by one-third.

There are numerous guides and videos for people to improve and 'greenify' their driving skills - and everyone will benefit from a better-driving you.

Oh, as for that $300,000 diamond on the Formula One car's nose cone in the 2004 Monaco Grand Prix - the one used by Austrian driver Christian Klien. It disappeared, never to be seen again, after he crashed on Lap One.

Impact: More efficient driving will save over 5% of vehicle emissions.
Difficulty: Easy.
Money-saving: Yes, £1k+
Action: Read or watch efficient driving guide books or videos.

I Do This Already  **I Choose This Task** ☐

Live Like a Millionaire Time Your Purchases and Buy in Bulk

In a very happy coincidence, it appears that many of the best traits of actual millionaires are exactly the same things that are seen in people who care for the environment. The vast majority of millionaires are almost the polar opposite of what we traditionally think a millionaire should be. Survey after survey shows most millionaires dislike waste, love making things last, tend to make few unnecessary or impulse purchases, don't follow fads and fashion, put experiences over 'things', avoid too much TV and surfing online, love what they do, work hard, are prone to helping charities, drive normal cars, buy quality and durability over quantity, and don't live in over expensive, super-flash homes. This last one is best exemplified by a man who has continuously been in the Top Ten Richest People In The World lists for every year of this century, Warren Buffet, the so-called 'Sage of Omaha'. He is so rich ($97 billion at the time of writing) that if he was a country he would be worth more than the European nation of Iceland. Even so, he still lives in the same house he bought for $31,500 in 1958.

One other similarity between millionaires and those who care about the environment is timing. If you want to make, or keep, your money, then buy at the best times. If you want to help the planet, do exactly the same.

Some items are cheaper at certain times of the year, month, week, or even day. Winter coats are almost always cheaper in summer, Christmas decorations are always cheaper in January, perishables are always cheaper at the end of the day, and flights are normally cheapest when booked for a Tuesday around midday or on any Friday 13th!

There is normally one promotion for most items each year in stores and supermarkets. Therefore, if an item is not urgently perishable, like tea, coffee, gin, whisky, beans, soup, toilet roll, toothpaste, shampoo, etc., and the price is good, then, if you have storage, bulk up and buy for the whole year. This may seem counter-intuitive to helping the environment but it works because it cuts down on time, packaging, and dozens of unnecessary trips.

Combining shopping/errands instead of doing them individually and shopping once a week, rather than every day, makes a big difference. Just one pound of extra temptation on each shop means people who shop every day will spend £365 extra a year, while those who go once a week will spend £52 extra a year. Over £300 saved, plus even bigger savings on transport, time, and energy. Time your purchases, organise your shopping, know exactly what you want to buy and stick to it and, if possible, buy in bulk.

Every country has different best purchasing times but, as a simple guide, the year tends to work out as follows: January (bedding, furniture, paint, towels, gym membership, Christmas items); February (winter clothes, boots, chocolate); March (luggage, perfume, jewellery); April (skis, laptops, DIY); May (fuel, holidays); June (power tools); July (canned food); August (shares, office supplies, school clothes, swimwear); September (garden furniture, backpacks); October (camping gear, plants, last minute holidays, flights, lawn mowers, mobile phones, bikes); November (wedding dresses, TV's and electronics, boats, golf clubs); December (cars, property, wines).

As for Black Friday, try not to join the hype. This environmental disaster of a day has been studied enough to show that 85% of its big 'sale' items had the same or lower prices within six months either side of the event.

Impact: Reduction of unnecessary purchases saves resources.
Difficulty: Easy.
Money-saving: Yes. £300+
Action: Save purchases for the best times in the year. Buy in bulk where possible.

I Do This Already  **I Choose This Task**

Live a Make-up Free Year

There is a phenomenon in the retail industry called the 'Lipstick Effect', which suggests that as an economy goes into recession or there is a disaster of some kind, while sales of most things will drop, some items, that people logically assume would also drop, actually see a mini-boom. The expression was first coined by cosmetics billionaire Leonard Lauder, who noted that after the 9/11 Terrorist attacks, sales of lipstick rose significantly. Lipstick, and cosmetics in general, it appears, are very important to consumers.

Cosmetics have, for thousands of years, been so vital to (mostly) women they were literally worth dying for. In Renaissance Europe, the upper classes, such as England's Queen Elizabeth I, were using daily a foundation made with mercury and a make-up made from lead and arsenic. All poisonous to humans! The chronicles of Elizabeth's latter years are filled with descriptions of her ailments and oddities. Most of which can today be explained as a result of her use, and ingestion, of toxin filled cosmetics.

Today, an avid daily lipstick wearer can expect to get through one lipstick per month, that's around 2g of the 3.5g lipstick bullet in the tube, though most people use considerably less. The most dedicated will reapply lipstick after every drink, meal, and some whenever they have a spare moment. The lipstick they are replacing will have had to go somewhere else in the first place. Much is left on glasses, cups, partners, friends, clothes, etc., but, depending on the wearer, a good portion, possibly 25%, will end up being eaten. The average woman on the planet will live until the age of 76, which means, if they were a serious lipstick wearer they could potentially have ingested 58 years worth of lipstick (58yrs x 12months x 0.5g), equal to 348 grams or the equivalent of over six Snickers bars in weight.

In today's modern and knowledgeable world things like lead, arsenic, and mercury have been removed and banned from cosmetics but there are a great many other ingredients that can be added that are not exactly 'beautiful'. Among the most concerning are fluorosurfactants known as PFAS, a group of 9000 or so man-made compounds better known as 'Forever Chemicals' because they don't degrade naturally. Worse, they have been found in water supplies and in the blood of wildlife - and humans. They are also linked to several serious health conditions such as kidney cancer and thyroid disease.

Sadly, a recent University of Notre Dame study of 231 cosmetics sold in North America discovered that 52% likely contained PFAS. The highest percentage of PFAS was found in 82% of waterproof mascaras, while lip products had 55%, concealers 36%, and foundations 63%.

One great way of not joining in with this great game of Cosmetic Russian Roulette would be for people to only use or buy cosmetics that can guarantee they use zero PFAS. Of course, a much simpler option would be to take a break (say 12 months) from the use of all cosmetics.

Yes, it has been said - no cosmetics for a whole year. No foundation, no mascara, no lipstick, or lip gloss, no concealers, no eyeliners, no blush, no primers, no perfumes - while allowing just simple soaps and shampoos.

Hard as hell for most people. It might be easier for some people to get rid of their boyfriend/girlfriend/husband/wife/partner or dog/cat than it would their favourite make-up. That said, ridding the world of cosmetics, even temporarily, while the industry sort out their ingredients issues would instantly remove a whole layer of pollutants from the world.

Impact: Reduction of PFAS entering the environment and humans.
Difficulty: Easy, but mentally hard.
Money-saving: Yes £300+
Action: Stop using make-up and perfumes for exactly 12 months.

I Do This Already  **I Choose This Task** ☐

Is Your Pension or Bank Wrecking the Planet?

The Romans seriously appreciated their military. After all, from one small nation state their army helped build an Empire that stretched from Rome to include all of Italy, France, Spain, southern Germany, and most of Britain, the Balkans, Greece, Turkey, the Caucasus, North Africa from Morocco to Egypt, and swathes of the Middle East into Arabia.

In return for their long service, Roman soldiers were traditionally awarded a grant of land after 25 years on which to finish their days. In 13BC, Emperor Augustus changed the system so that every soldier who completed 25 years was given the equivalent of 13 years' wages as a lump sum. Soon after, he created a fund to pay for these retiring soldiers, the 'aeririum militaire' - essentially, the world's first formal lump sum pension scheme. Of course, life expectancy wasn't anywhere near the 73 years for the average human these days, it was just 37, but even so, its payment gave a welcome level of comfort, and respect, for those who had been loyal to the Roman Empire.

It would not be until 19 centuries later, in 1889, that the first true modern state pension came into place when Otto von Bismarck, the man who unified Germany, introduced a pension for workers who reached the age of 70.

Since then, the amount of money now held by pension funds around the world, according to the OECD, is $35 trillion. That is enough money to pay the wages of an Army of over 65 million US soldiers for the next 25 years ($21,420 per year for Private E1). Pension funds are mighty, and how the funds, and the money controlled by banks and the rest of the financial world is spent can make a massive difference to our planet - good or bad.

Most people work hard for their money. Some running two, maybe three jobs or doing all the overtime and weekend work they can to pay their way - or save for a rainy day or financial goal. They get up early, work late, run a tight budget, even do without, and they have to - as only one-eighth of the world's population are in the luxurious position of having a financial worth, including any property, of more than $100,000.

After all this effort, what do we do when we finally have money left over at the end of each month? Well, the vast majority of us hand it over to the financial services industry - the banks, the pension funds, the investment funds, etc.. Many of these organisations then go on to use our money to fund planet crushing projects for the sake of their profits.

Those who can honestly say they know what is happening to their savings, their pension pot, their investment funds, even their checking account money, can stop reading now - you are one in a thousand. Most of us have no idea - and that is a big problem for the environment as lots of our money is used to fund not particularly Earth-friendly projects and companies.

The Rainforest Action Alliance suggest that in the five years following the Paris COP21 climate change agreement, signed by 196 countries, the world's 60 biggest banks financed fossil fuels to the tune of $3,800,000,000,000.

We can stop this lunacy. It is not difficult to find an actual 'green' bank, one that has a 100% commitment solely to environment friendly financing. If you invest, or have a pension fund, then it is not too difficult to work out (or ask) where your money is being used. If you have one that is investing in coal, oil or gas, or any environmentally dodgy area, is this really where you want to keep your money? The money you are saving for a brighter future.

Impact: Billions of dollars removed from planet crushing projects and instead invested in environment friendly ones.
Difficulty: Moderately easy.
Money-saving: No change.
Action: Look at your finances and see how your money is being used.

I Choose This Task ☐

Keep Your Cool! Turn the Temperature Down

One of the least cool jobs in the United States must be to work as a Ranger in the Death Valley National Park in California. It's not that the work is bad, in fact a Park Ranger job seems like great fun. It's simply, literally, not cool - because the temperature there has been recorded at a world beating 130 degrees Fahrenheit (54.4 degrees Celsius). This happened at the Furnace Creek Visitors Center on 9 July 2021. That is hot. So hot you could put a pan on any flat surface in the open and fry a steak. It is little wonder the area has warning signs Saying 'STOP Extreme Heat Danger' and advises people not to walk in the area after 10am in the morning. It's not called Death Valley for fun - at the time of writing three people have already died in the area in the past year due to the extreme heat.

In complete contrast, the coldest temperature ever recorded in the USA is the -79.8 degrees Fahrenheit (-62 degrees Celsius) taken on 23 January 1971 at Prospect Creek in Alaska, a place just south of another National Park, the Gates of the Arctic National Park and Preserve. That is so cold that if you threw a bucket of boiling water into the air it would freeze before it touched the ground (the so-called Mpemba Effect). That's cold!

Hot, cold, or in-between, America's Park Rangers must have varied closets trying to dress for the temperature extremes of their National Parks.

The temperature of a place makes all the difference to our lives. Fortunately, humans have managed to work out ways of capturing energy to allow us to stay warm on cold days, and cool on hot days. However, this heating and cooling has a cost - creating two-fifths of all household CO_2 emissions.

When you are talking temperature, the reality is that even one degree of difference can make all the difference. Since the start of the Industrial Revolution our planet has warmed by only 1 degree Celsius and we know exactly the damage that alone has caused. All we have to do is look out of our windows. We can all see our changing climate, floods, drought, rising sea levels, increased storms and the mass extinctions of different lifeforms - so much havoc from one small change in temperature.

When world bodies come together to address this problem, they have no actual 'big plan' to get levels back to where they were, instead agreeing only to try and limit global warming by rising another 2 degrees Celsius in the distant future. That's like doctors telling a person who's just been shot: *'The bad news is we can't fix you to the level you once were. The good news is we've set non-binding targets in the hope you won't get shot more than twice again in the next thirty years'*.

This is a situation where individuals need to drive the change and there are some very simple measures for home heating and cooling we can all do. The first is to change the supply of energy to one that is not coal, oil, or gas powered. If you already have electric air-con and heating then changing to a 'renewable energy only' deal with your electricity supplier instantly reduces the problem. If not, then installing geothermal (ground heat-pump), solar, or other on-site renewable energy source is a longer-term solution.

If you can't make these changes then reducing the thermostat by just one degree Celsius shouldn't upset your comfort. If you also reduce the thermostat by 10 degrees Celsius when you go out then it will be possible to reduce your emissions (and your bills) by around 5 to 15%.

Impact: Reduction in home heating CO2 emissions by 5% plus.
Difficulty: Easy.
Money-saving: Yes (5%+ off bills).
Action: Turn thermostat down and change energy contract to '100% renewable'.

I Do This Already  **I Choose This Task**

Help the Research

For every yin there is a yang, for every black there is a white, for every positive there is a negative. For every Nobel Prize, there is a sneaky cheeky cousin - the Ig Nobel Prize - an annual global award that celebrates the more unusual research conducted on our planet. Research, according to the organisers that 'first makes people laugh, and then makes them think'.

Since 1991 the Ig Nobel Prize has highlighted some very odd research, such as Robert Matthews of Aston University who won the 1996 Physics Prize for work on Murphy's Law and why toast tends to fall to the floor on the buttered side. In statistics, the 1998 Prize went to Jerald Bain and Kerry Siminoski whose work at the University of Alberta finally dispelled the myth that suggested there was a link between Height, Penile Length and Foot Size. In Veterinary Medicine, the 2009 Prize went to Cath Douglas and Peter Rowlinson of Newcastle University for research showing that cows who have been given names yield more milk. The 2019 Prize for Economics went to Timothy Voss, Habip Gedik and Andreas Voss of Radboud University in the Netherlands for their work on which country's paper currency was the dirtiest and carried the most micro-organisms (the winner was Romania's Leu). In 2021, the winner of the Prize for Economics was Pavlo Blavatskyy of Montpelier Business School in France for his work on correlating a link between the percentage of overweight and obese politicians in a country's government and that country's level of corruption.

Research is important, sometimes even the odd stuff (at least one Ig Nobel winner, Sir Andre K Geim, went on to win a real Nobel Prize), and when it comes to the environment, the more we can learn, the better we will become at addressing the problems our planet is facing.

Most of us may feel as though there is little we can do to change the environment, but this is simply not true. Even simply getting involved in a minor way in the varying types of environmental research can make a big difference down the line. Think about it, how do we actually know that the number of sparrow birds, for example, have dropped by 60% in the UK? Part of the answer is that over one million people, many of them schoolchildren, take part in the Big Garden Birdwatch each January and literally count the birds they see. The Royal Society for the Protection of Birds (RSPB) can then allocate resources to finding out why these things are happening.

In the United States, the National Oceanic and Atmospheric Administration (NOAA), as an example, work with volunteers across the country as daily weather observers, storm spotters, and transcribers of old ship logs dating back to 1850, for information on weather or sea ice. They even have volunteers playing a part by just having a smart phone and uploading an app that measures the magnetic field in their location.

There are so many surveys and research work needed all around the world to work out what's happening to our wildlife, rivers, seas, trees, atmosphere, and a million other things. Counting butterflies, birdwatching, locating hedgehogs, even locating whales at sea so ships can avoid them, all need volunteers. Picking litter from beaches may not seem like research, but if we analyse that litter, we know exactly what is being thrown away, and can then make decisions about how to reduce or stop those specific litter items.

If you get a chance to help environment research, be it a survey, opinion poll, count, or other useful and fulfilling thing - do it! Most are good fun, very social, and give us a more accurate picture of what's really going on in our world.

Impact: Varies from small to massive dependent on the research topic.
Difficulty: Normally easy, and fun.
Money-saving: Yes-No-Maybe.
Action: If you hear of research being carried out, get involved.

I Do This Already ★ I Choose This Task ☐

Get Busy - Work Smart

There is little doubt that most people are aware of the name Elon Musk, or possibly Isambard Kingdom Brunel, or Gen Leslie Groves. These names have one very big thing in common - they are regarded as being perfect examples of 'busy'. Elon Musk (think Paypal, SpaceX, Tesla, Solar City), Isambard Kingdom Brunel (think engineer of the Great Western Railway, first tunnel under a major river, first ocean going ship made of iron), and Gen Leslie Groves (think boss for construction of The Pentagon, the world's largest office building, and director of The Manhattan Project). These people are the essence of 'busy', 'can do', and 'do it now' - and are celebrated as such.

Pablo Picasso was busy. Very busy. When he died in 1973 he left behind over 50,000 works of art, including 1,885 paintings, 1,228 sculptures, 12,000 drawings, thousands of prints and ceramics, plus dozens of sketchbooks, rugs and tapestries. If he had completed one piece of art every single day as an adult, he would have needed to live to the age of 155 to do what he did in his actual 91 years on Earth. Even with that workload, plus having to deal with life in Paris during World Wars One and Two, the Spanish Civil War, two wives, three long term partners, plus a stream of mistresses, he still found time to also take up poetry, compiling over 300 poems.

Barbara Cartland, the step-grandmother of Princess Diana and the most prolific novelist in history, wrote 723 books in her lifetime, yet still found time to be heavily involved in politics as a local councillor.

Busy gets things done. The Reverend William James Kennedy, one of Her Majesty's Inspectors of Schools, correctly noted in 1851 during the time of Queen Victoria, 'If you want any business done for you, you should ask a busy person to do it, not a person of leisure'.

We all think we are busy. Indeed, as Kanye West pointed out so modestly in a 2006 interview 'I feel like I'm too busy writing history to read it', when asked if he ever just zoned out with a good book.

In reality, our 'busy-ness' normally falls under something called the Pareto Principle, also known as the 80-20 rule. This essentially suggests that of the 100% of any project, the most effective 80% can be done in 20% of the time. If we can harness the power of the 20% that creates 80% of the result then we can end up being prolific - but to do this we also need to get rid of many of the inefficient things (like red tape, constant distractions or procrastination) that fill 80% in time and effort to get only a 20% result.

A good example of using the 80% less productive time more effectively can be found in Picasso's poetry. He seldom titled his poems, merely making note of the date and his location. No sitting for ages (part of the 80%) trying to encapsulate the full meaning of the poem in a single line. He simply used that time to 'do' more poems, or art.

Much of the world thinks it is the industrious and busy who cause problems for the environment - but our environment is affected far more by the docile and unmotivated than the active and interested. Lazy people make lazy decisions, they continually buy fast food instead of cook, drive rather than walk, buy new stuff rather than mend, or give candy rather than attention. Crucially, almost every environmental problem starts because someone is too lazy to take ownership. Chernobyl started when one work shift passed a crucial safety test on to the unprepared next work shift. In a similar manner, people not removing their litter from beaches, means even more plastic in our oceans.

Get busy, take ownership, and be smart with your time.

Impact: Significant - especially so if you work in a nuclear power station.
Difficulty: Change from un-busy to busy is hard, but rewarding.
Money-saving: Yes £100+
Action: Work harder, work smarter, and work longer if it brings you enjoyment and satisfaction.

I Choose This Task

Don't Be A Drip! Fix That Leak

There aren't too many people who can say they haven't watched the 1990 comedy film *Home Alone* - the story of a young boy having to fend off burglars at his home after accidentally being left behind by his family when they go on a Christmas vacation to Paris. The film, which made a reported $477 million at the box office, is now a Christmas classic, but like the films *Die Hard*, *Trading Places* and *Gremlins*, there have been many heated conversations by cinema lovers about whether it is actually a Christmas film at all (after all, are child abandonment, police ineptitude, burglary, stalking and extreme violence, really what Christmas is all about?).

The premise that any child could be left behind by their family as they embark on a vacation may seem far-fetched but as the author of this very book had exactly the same thing, in reverse, happen to him as a child, this book is always going to have a small affinity with young Kevin McCallister (played by Macaulay Culkin).

The reason *Home Alone* is mentioned is that the burglars in the film, Harry and Marv, were, in legal terms, signature criminals. They referred to themselves as the 'Wet Bandits' and their calling card after every burglary was to leave the taps running to eventually flood out the basements of the homes from which they had committed their crime. This 'signature' eventually helped convict the pair of many of the other burglaries they had committed in the area.

In terms of the environment, the reality is that a leaking tap or burst pipe anywhere these days is as anti-social to society and the planet as the Wet Bandits could ever have been. A leaking pipe, if not fixed, literally steals the life blood of our planet ... water.

Coincidentally, Harry, one of the 'Wet Bandits' in *Home Alone* was played by Joe Pesci, who, alongside Marisa Tomei, is in probably one of the greatest 'leaking tap' film scenes (yes, they exist) in Hollywood history, in the 1992 film *My Cousin Vinny*. In the scene they share together, the dripping tap was not turned off. In real life that can have big consequences.

According to the United States Geological Survey (USGS) a tap, dripping one time per second, would add up to 86,000 drips per day which is equivalent to 21.6 litres (5.7 gallons). Over a year, if left untouched, that simple little dripping tap would lose 7,884 litres (2,083 gallons) of water which is enough water to run an efficient modern dishwasher using 11 litres per run, a total of 716 times, or almost twice a day, every day. That dripping tap of 21.6 litres is also more than enough water for a family of ten people to get their recommended amount of drinking water each day.

On a world scale it is estimated that as much as 13.7% of all household water is wasted by leaks. In the United States the Environmental Protection Agency suggest that the average household accounts for nearly 10,000 gallons (37,854 litres) of water wasted every year and fixing these alone would save 10% of water bills.

Most big leaks don't come in the form of a simple dripping tap or showerhead, they tend to come from toilets (normally the valve seals) or outdoor leaks such as those from sprinkler systems, hose pipes and frozen/leaking/burst pipes.

If you have a water meter turn everything off and give it a check. If it still moves - you've become a 'wet bandit', wasting water and expensively paying the privilege for doing so.

If you have a leak .... fix it!

Impact: Possible reduction in use of over 10% of fresh water in households.
Difficulty: Moderate difficulty.
Money-saving: Yes. At minimum the price of 7,884 litres of water.
Action: Check water meter. Check for physical leaks. Get them fixed.

I Choose This Task

Be a Borrower ... and a Lender
Feel the Benefits of Sharing Things

Oh to be a teenager, sat in an English Literature class on a hot afternoon and advised by the teacher that you are about to start on yet another William Shakespeare play. This one is special, it's Hamlet, Shakespeare's longest play. Set in Denmark, it tells the story of Prince Hamlet's revenge against Claudius, the murderer of his father, who happens to also be his Uncle and, after marrying his mother Gertrude, is now also his stepfather. While most of the class are groaning at the thought of reading 30,557 words of original soap opera, there are a small percent who are absolutely giddy at the knowledge this is Shakespeare's greatest play - full of insight and wisdom. Oh yaay!

One of the classic, and most oft repeated lines from the play in the 420 plus years since it was written, is given by Polonius, a councillor to King Claudius, who advises Laertes, his France bound son, on how to conduct himself while away. Part of his advice is '... Neither a borrower nor a lender be; for loan oft loses both itself and friend, and borrowing dulls the edge of husbandry ...'

(In modern English, if you want to keep your friends, and your cash, never lend money, and if you want to keep on top of your finances, never borrow.)

Polonius was full of quotables, lines that are said every day a million times in modern society, such as: 'Brevity is the soul of wit', 'there's method in the madness', and 'be true to thine own self'. (Spoiler alert! - he still died)

Polonius was used by Shakespeare as an unimaginative and pompous fool, and while 'neither a borrower nor a lender be' might be great advice regarding cash, when it comes to today's climate crisis, a modern day bard would have added 'but it's fine to share stuff with other sharers'.

The big question is not 'whether' to be a borrower or a lender but 'when' to be a borrower and a lender - and why it is good for you and the planet.

Take, for example, a simple ladder. Most of its life it sits hung on a wall at the side of a garage, coming out for use on odd occasions such as when a roof tile comes off, gutters need cleaning, or a wall needs painting. It rarely sees any action on more than three days a year. That's not even one percent of its time doing what it was expensively built to do. It makes far more sense for just one household in a street of five houses, to own a ladder that can be used by all, than for five £400 ladders to be individually purchased. The cost in Earth's resources used also drops to just 20% of what it would have been had everyone done a 'what's mine is mine' act, and bought their own stuff.

If the four other neighbours each also own super-useful but occasionally used items, like jet-washers, trailers, tents, hedge cutters, lawn mowers, books, tools, DVD's, kayaks, etc., and in return allow you to use their stuff (responsibly), then everyone saves dollar and the planet breathes easier.

Naturally, a fair system of sharing has to be used. If people feel they can't share equitably with their neighbours, there are various apps available which make the sharing/bartering process easier.

Some local areas even have a shared stock of seldom used items that are purchased collectively and maintained for all to use.

In some cases, simple creativity helps. If there is a young person not sat reading Shakespeare all day, or one of your other neighbours has time to spare, then you and the rest of the neighbours can pay them so they can own a great lawnmower and cut everyone's grass on a regular basis.

TIP: However you share, always take a digital photograph of the borrower with the item so you know who's got it, and when they got it!

Impact: Reduces need for up to 80% of resources to be used on one particular item.
Difficulty: Easy (within boundaries).
Money-saving: Yes £100+
Action: Offer to share with responsible and trustworthy people who are equally prepared to share.

I Choose This Task ☐

Super Insulate Your Home and Make Super Savings

In 2012, an architect called Colin Usher and his wife Jenny bought a rundown detached house on a fairly standard street in the small town of West Kirby, near Liverpool, England. Within two years they had demolished the property and replaced it with a not too dissimilar looking residence to others on the same street. The main difference was simply that the heating, lighting, hot water and cooking for this new four-bedroomed home cost them less to run for a full year than the cost of going for just one meal at their local restaurant. That's roughly £75 - for a whole year.

The couple hadn't spent a fortune to build the new property, in fact their build cost was similar to other new homes in the area. However, they had used every insulation and eco trick in the book to make sure they were as close to carbon neutral as they could be on a tight budget.

The couple are not alone in building a super efficient home. Indeed there are hundreds of thousands of varying eco-friendly homes being built and lived in all over the planet. They are mentioned here as inspiration that a properly insulated home not only helps hold back climate change but can literally save thousands of pounds, dollars, euros, or whatever currency you love the most. In the UK, at the time of writing, comparing Colin and Jenny Usher's energy bills to the average four-bedroomed home in their local area, they will have saved over £1264 in their first year - or around £31,600 over the next 25 years.

No one is being asked to rebuild their home to reduce greenhouse gas emissions, but simply insulating our homes can make a massive difference.

Something like 19% of all greenhouse gas emissions come from heating up or cooling our homes and workplaces. If we reduced that figure even by half we could remove almost ten percent of greenhouse gas emissions altogether. In itself, this will not bring an end to climate change, but it's not a bad place to start - it will save tons of money - and is so easy for most people to do immediately.

There are many ways to make your home more energy efficient, but the biggest is to make sure your loft is well insulated. The UK energy company OVO Energy suggest that for a spend of just £300 on loft insulation it is possible to get a saving of £750 over five years (plus not adding an extra 610kg of carbon to the atmosphere each year).

It is estimated that around one-third of home heat is lost through the walls of badly insulated homes. This is equivalent to throwing away £33 for every £100 in your heating budget. Crazy! Especially when this can be remedied quickly and paid for from energy savings over an average of five years.

Other great energy efficiency tips are to install double or triple glazing, upgrade your boiler or AC unit, grow ivy on the outside walls of your home, invest in thicker curtains/drapes/blinds or even the old, tested, and incredibly cheap methods - screw down draughty floorboards, close doors, and use draught excluders. One very high tech and sensible move is to get a thermal image survey done of your property before you do anything. This will show exactly where you are losing heat - and money.

Best of all, in many countries, states, regions and cities there are schemes available, normally called something like Green Homes Grants, where you can get a contribution towards making your home more energy efficient.

Impact: Up to 10% reduction in all greenhouse gas emissions.
Difficulty: Moderately easy.
Money-saving: Yes, but over time.
Action: Have home checked for heat loss areas. Properly insulate them.

I Choose This Task ☐

Look at the Ingredients

It has been suggested that the easiest way to lose weight is to become interested in the environment. People tend to quickly find that almost everything they eat and drink 'ruins the planet' in some way or another. Rice production is the biggest producer of methane from any human plant agriculture. Peaches, mangoes, and dates suck valuable water out of our ecosystem at a rate of between 1200 to 3000 litres for every single kilo of fruit. Farmed fish, especially salmon, helps pollute our seas from their use of chemicals and antibiotics. Cultivation of palm oil, which is in almost every food, destroys rainforest and quickly leads to massive soil erosion.

Coffee cultivation helps kill birds and rainforests and then uses masses of energy in roasting. Meat creates massive amounts of methane, and uses up land that could feed many more people if used for crops. Sugar removes the organic carbon content of soil, adds to climate change, and fuels a diabetes and obesity epidemic. Our beloved chocolate is destroying the planet as its cultivation is happening at the expense of traditional mixed farming and creates a forced encroachment into equatorial forests. Even the cereals we eat may be genetically modified. And don't get environmentalists started on millennials love of avocados. How can any of us sleep?

It's all so bleak, so dark, so sad, so dystopian.

Or is it?

Yes, the planet's food production and distribution system is very destructive to the environment. But, it's not something that can't be fixed. The real problem is that the suppliers of our food are normally super efficient, very powerful, and tend to go to the cheapest global sources so they can do three things: grow their market share, make their products cheaper, and increase their profit margins. And most people simply accept this as being 'normal'.

One of the simplest things we can do to improve the planet is to look at the label of every food we purchase. Not just a glimpse, but study exactly what ingredients are going into something that we are then going to put inside our bodies, and the bodies of our family and friends, or anyone else who eats our food. What are those E numbers about? Why does this product have palm oil, or sugar, or so much salt? We have to stop thinking of our bodies as trash cans and get back to regarding them as temples. We should also consider where the ingredients came from, their journey, and what impact our use of these ingredients will have on the environment.

Take coffee, as an example. There is no way on hell some people are going to stop drinking the world's third most favourite drink (sorry coffee drinkers, but water, then tea, are first and second). Some might still drink coffee even if it was the sole cause of climate change! But change can come if people move to shade grown coffee or coffee that is certified as being ethical and sustainable. Whatever we eat or drink, the more we learn about it, the more we can decide if it should play a part in our lives, and the life of our planet.

It goes without saying that buying raw, natural, locally sourced and in-season food from respected local stores and suppliers is far preferable to over-packaged, over-marketed, and over-seas food from super-large corporate owned brands sold to us via dominant and market controlling supermarket chains.

It is worth noting that checking ingredients is not just about foods, but many non-food items as well, like cosmetics, clothing, cars, housing, even furniture. It's not difficult to ask (or find out) where the oak in that oak furniture came from, or if that lipstick has any PFAS?

And if a brand or store can't answer questions about their own products then don't forget... If in doubt, opt out!

Impact: Large impact as companies go greener to keep market share.
Difficulty: Quite a chore as it involves research.
Money-saving: Yes-No-Maybe.
Action: Just check ingredients or source - and likely impact of that food/product on you or the environment.

I Choose This Task ☐

Eat Like it's World War Two Exercise Like it's Lockdown

The world's largest humanitarian organisation and the Nobel Peace Prize winner of 2020, is the United Nations World Food Programme (WFP). Headquartered in Rome, the WFP has 20,600 staff operating in 84 countries and helps bring food and assistance to millions of people trying to recover from conflict, disasters, and the effects of climate change. On any given day the organisation has 5,600 trucks, 30 ships, and 100 aircraft on the move everywhere from Afghanistan to Zimbabwe.

Incredibly, the WFP is funded entirely by voluntary donations, its largest donors (the 13 countries giving over $50 million each in 2021) being the USA, Germany, Canada, Japan, Sweden, Norway, United Kingdom, Saudi Arabia, Australia, Switzerland, South Korea, France, and the Netherlands.

The main reason for mentioning the World Food Programme is that they do great things and deserve recognition. There is also another reason. They publish an average figure for the cost of a single food ration. In other words, they have the monetary price of keeping a person alive for a day with sufficient and varied food to supply 2100 calories and basic micronutrients such as vitamins A, iron, iodine and zinc.

That price in US dollars, **the price of a human life**, is not even one single dollar - it's just **61 cents**.

To put this 61 cents into context, it is worth noting that the average American, according to the Food & Drug Administration (FDA) will throw away a third of their food every year. The value of this wasted food alone is worth over $161 billion - or enough to pay for 264 billion daily food rations - enough to keep 100 million people fed for over seven years.

It is evident that as much of our world live in a place of food excess that has never been matched in history, a vast segment of the world (811 million people according to the WFP) go to bed hungry each night - that's the equivalent of 21 times the population of Canada.

Logically, one very simple way of reducing this food mismatch, and at the same time helping spread the resources of the planet more evenly, would be for those on the excess side of the equation to try to live on far less calories than at present. Not the 2100 calories of a WFP food ration, but something similar to the more than adequate 3000 calories a day of the UK food rationing system of World War Two. A period most nutritionists suggest was the healthiest in British history. This was also a time when UK children were at their fittest and the elderly were dying at a later age than the generation before, not the other way around as we see in the country today.

One simple way to adjust the imbalance is to make small changes in diet - nothing drastic - and work out what local and seasonal foods can be included in meals. Reduce overeating, having set mealtimes, planned meals, and if people are eating like it's WW2 then including things like vegetables, oats and pulses, plus locally grown fruits and berries. A key factor is the reduction of meat as well as cutting back on fats, sugars and excess alcohol.

It is said the route to good health is quicker through the kitchen than the gym - but exercise is also vitally important - and inspires the need for better food. As people discovered on seeing old friends after the early Covid-19 lockdowns - those who wanted to change could do so incredibly quickly.

Making a small positive food change for yourself can have a big spin-off for the hungry of the world. Eat like it's WW2 and keep fit like it's lockdown.

Impact: If money spent on wasted food was diverted - it could end hunger.
Difficulty: Hard, but satisfying.
Money-saving: Yes £500+
Action: Keep to a nutritional diet and have plenty of exercise. Buy only food you need, not want.

I Do This Already ★ I Choose This Task ☐

Go Solar!

The Earth is BIG. Very, very, BIG. Minuscule when compared to the rest of the Milky Way and not even a dot on a dot on a dot on an even more minuscule dot when compared to the Universe. But really big when compared to humans - and it does have something we've so far not found on any other planet. Life.

If you stood on the equator and started walking for 10,000 steps each day (which is roughly 8km or 5miles) in a straight line to either the east or west, and could walk on water, it would take you around 5009 days before you had walked right around the world and ended up back at the same place you started. That's 13 years and 8 months. Less time if you walk more steps, more time if you can't walk on water.

Earth is also literally teeming with people. All 7.9 billion of us. If you could shake hands with everyone alive right now at a super rapid speed of two seconds per handshake, then, doing so for 12 hours every day, it would take 1000 years to complete, by which time everyone you had wanted to shake hands with would be long gone and replaced by even more people.

The energy needed to supply our planet is massive, presently 600 quadrillion BTU* a year. But here's the thing, we orbit a pretty impressive, and free, energy source - the sun - and it is expected to last for another 5 billion years. According to the US Department of Energy the light the sun shines on our planet for a period of just 90 minutes is enough to supply every single bit of energy we presently use on the planet in a whole year.

Sunlight is literally hitting over half the planet at any one moment. All we need to do is decide whether to capture that energy and use it for our needs - or let it go to waste and use climate destroying energy sources instead.

**BTU is British Thermal Unit, a measurement equal to the energy needed to increase the temperature of a pound of water by 1 degree Fahrenheit*

Solar has come a long way since its early days powering our calculators back in the seventies. Whole communities and homes are now supplied with energy quite cheaply from the use of solar farms and household solar panels.

Supply of the raw material (sunlight) to make energy is free. Solar panels also work almost anywhere on the surface of the planet, whether at sea, in the middle of a desert, even space. Placed on a roof they also add an extra layer of insulation. They are also built to withstand extreme weather.

The downside of solar is that it is initially expensive to install. However, as the normal break-even point is eleven years, and most solar panels are expected to last for 25 years with minimal maintenance, that extra 14 years is, as they say, 'all gravy, baby'. Yes, 14 plus years of zero-cost energy.

Other benefits include the fact that, as solar energy can be fed back into the electricity grid, individuals can sell some of the energy they make at the same time as helping the security and consistency of the network. A very nice social bonus is that, as most of the work on solar is installation and occasional maintenance, normally conducted by local workers, it creates local jobs.

One obvious problem with solar is it doesn't really work at night or too well in the absolute depths of winter. This can be eased by battery storage, saving up excess energy for a 'rainy day' (actually solar still takes energy on rainy days, so saving for a 'very dark day' might be more appropriate).

For the planet, the use of solar panels on homes means that the loss in transporting electricity from far off power stations saves roughly 3% to 5% of all the energy used. Solar also doesn't create waste or noise pollution.

One final thing worth noting is that at least one in-depth study in the USA reported that solar panels add at least $15,000 plus to the value of a home.

Impact: Removes all carbon emissions from creation of home electricity.
Difficulty: Easy, but initially expensive.
Money-saving: Yes. £10k+
Action: Cost out your present home energy over 25 years. Compare to using solar installation. Buy.

I Choose This Task

Use a Smart Meter and do an Energy Audit of Your Home

Possibly one of the freakiest TV ad campaigns for a long time was about helping to reduce energy with the purpose of saving - you guessed it - planet Earth. The campaign was run in the UK by Smart Energy GB, a not-for-profit government backed campaign to encourage people to install smart meters in their homes. Nothing freaky so far, but the campaign was fronted by a CGI (Computer Generated Imagery) created 'deepfake' of the long deceased theoretical physicist, Albert Einstein. In the ad campaign, we see a very much alive Einstein, who left this world nearly seven decades ago, in his prime, and in his bath, checking out his instagram profile, then roaming the British countryside telling the world how much he loves wind.

For anyone with a love of Einstein and his brilliance this was sacrilege - to create a living version of a long dead hero to push a marketing campaign was too much to bear. Reddit and Twitter users had a frenzy!

Einstein is not alone in having been deepfaked back into existence for a TV ad, Hollywood actress Audrey Hepburn found herself peddling Galaxy chocolate twenty years after she died, while Bruce Willis, who is not even dead and wasn't even in the country, recently found himself looking much younger in a Russian TV ad for a telecoms company.

Bizarre! Weird! Spooky! And other than the last one, the whole idea of 'deepfake' appearances brings a new meaning to the expression 'making a living'.

Anyway, back to our deepfaked Einstein. The campaign had several different ads but the one that resonated the most suggested that if every household in the country used a smart meter, the CO2 savings Britain could make would be equivalent to the savings made by 70 million trees.

The fact that 24.2 million households and small businesses in the UK and 107 million homes in the USA now have smart meters suggests the message of just how beneficial they can be is getting across.

Most people, on setting up their smart meter, are quite amazed to discover that the innocent looking towel warmer in their bathroom is taking up more energy than their freezer, or that their hairdryer can use up twice as much energy as their microwave.

Lots of us have zero idea which electrical items in our homes use up the most energy. For those who don't have a smart meter and can't work it out, then, according to the Centre For Sustainable Energy, in the average home it's normally an electric shower, followed, in order of energy required, by water heater, kettle, tumble dryer, electric fire, oven, then hairdryer.

In the main we take little interest in the energy output of the items we use the most ... but we should. If you have a smart meter you can do an energy audit - which sounds really boring but is normally quite enlightening when you understand what you are spending money on. It is quite easy to work out what energy is used where around the home. So, before a smart meter, most people concentrate on turning lights on and off to save energy, but after a smart meter is fitted, they see that lighting normally only takes up 5% of energy usage. Much bigger savings are to be made in home heating at roughly 43%, water heating 19%, home cooling 8%, electronics 5%, cooking 4%, refrigeration 3%, computers 2%, and other stuff 11%.

Few of us will ever be as intelligent as Albert Einstein, but if using a simple smart meter helps each of us to save money and be as CO_2 reducing as a tree then that's pretty bright.

Impact: Helps avoid the CO_2 equivalent of 2 million trees for every one million households that use smart meter.
Difficulty: Super easy.
Money-saving: Yes £300+
Action: Ask energy supplier for a smart meter. They are free in many areas.

I Choose This Task

Stop Buying Everything Online

If you work in retail sales, one of the first lessons you learn is that 'people buy from people' and if you can get a friendly conversation going with a prospective buyer there's a better chance it can be converted into a sale. That's one of the reasons sales people have a tendency to pounce on shoppers with conversation starters like, 'How can I help you?' or 'What is it you're looking for today?'. And customers know it, most of us feel ensnared from the moment we reply with a meek, 'Just looking.' or 'I'm ok thanks.'.

Today, as 20% of all retail sales in the world are made online, that group of real sales staff has transformed into an army of virtual sales staff in our phones or on our laptops. They 'converse' with us via e-mail, text, messages, and notifications. They are kind enough to tell us things like, 'There is 25% off.', a particular product they know we will like or offer things to us 'exclusively'. If we are especially gullible, they may even get in touch to congratulate us, like we've just won an Olympic medal, on being 'eligible to apply' for their membership or discount card - even a credit card to buy their products. They are conversing, like those sales guys in the stores, but we're not even in their store, or had even realised we wanted any more of their stuff. In the office, on holiday, even sat in the bath, they are there to encourage our involvement. Even worse, if we do buy something, we may end up being corralled into signing up for a monthly or yearly subscription that allows cheaper delivery, better discounts or supposed VIP or Gold service.

Sorry, but online retailers have us owned. They have big departments filled with smart people, behavioural psychologists, even AI, using all their time working out how to relieve us of our money. We may feel powerless against this marketing onslaught, but there is some relief - the off switch.

Do we really need to buy one single $2 nail clipper direct from Hong Kong? Are we online buying a new vacuum cleaner six months after we bought the last because it is a Black Friday bargain? Are we expecting immediate delivery? Do we know the names of every delivery driver in our area?

STOP! For the love of our sanity and the planet, we need to give it a break.

The idea that planes are flying the globe carrying our new hairbrushes, or thousands of different vans are driving up and down the country delivering single items to the same address every single day is environmentally crazy. Yes, purchase online for specialist stuff at a good price - but getting things we don't need, or could buy as part of a normal shop, is lazy management.

If we budget our money then it is also worthwhile budgeting our online time. One great method of controlling our online purchases is to give them a particular time in our diary. Save all our online comparison and purchase ideas for the week (or month) and sort them out at a time that is convenient to do it all at once. And never feel pressured into buying a time-dated offer or by supposed 'limited availability'. It is surprising how little of what we were going to buy, we will actually still want to buy a few days later - and most items will still be available. That old 'cold light of day' stuff really works.

Giving retailers our default payment information making us able to make one-click purchases is also not a great way to reduce climate change. Some 41% of people have abandoned at least one online sale in the past year. That figure drops by a third for those who have a one-click payment process, suggesting that even when we may not really want a product, and the planet needs to save its resources, the super-efficient process has us sorted and paid before any 'changed my mind' process can turn into a cancel.

Impact: Stops resources being used to make things people don't actually want.
Difficulty: Moderate to Very Hard.
Money-saving: Yes £100+
Action: Make fixed time for internet purchases. Remove default payments.

I Choose This Task ☐

Choose Quality Over Quantity

The author of this book has a good friend in England who thinks Christmas isn't a real Christmas unless it includes the finest wine and plenty of mince pies - a traditional Christmas food popular in the UK, Australia, and New Zealand.

Every year, normally before December, he visits many of his friends for a chit-chat. Nothing too elaborate, a simple flying visit, and he always takes a newly purchased pack of mince pies as a gift they can have with their catch-up tea or coffee. Lovely gesture and part of the conversation always includes everyone's view on this year's mince pie offering.

He does this so he can hit two birds with one stone. He loves the catch-up, but he also uses the opportunity to sample the annual mince pie offerings from each different bakery and supermarket. For every visit he buys a completely different pack of mince pies. Within a few short weeks after catching up with close friends, he has a good idea what he should get them for Christmas AND he knows which mince pies he likes the best. The upshot is that during Christmas he always has the best mince pies - tried and tested. Coincidentally, he also has the best wine - sorted out during his summer holiday every year to an old pal's house in France (but that's another story).

Strange? Yes? Possibly? But so practical, so multitasking, and so pleasant for the people he visits. Interestingly, this friend is also the most unassuming multi-millionaire you could ever meet. No flash car, no super fashionable clothes, no supersized blinged out mansion - just a robust Land Rover, very practical and hardwearing clothes, and a very modest but comfortable home.

It is sometimes incredibly hard to find the 'quality' in a 'quantity' world, but occasionally, as our mince pie millionaire has shown us, there is fun, and reward, to be found seeking quality in even the most trivial of things.

There are a couple of sayings worth noting. The first is that it is normally only while attending their own third or fourth wedding ceremony that people finally realise that quality is always better than quantity. The second is that people who don't understand quality always find themselves chasing quantity. In either case, don't let this be you. Our environment can't take it.

The difficulty with trying to find quality over quantity tends to be that it is not quick enough for most people. It normally involves a bit of research, a bit of thinking time, or worse, it occasionally means you have to save up!

If you can, be the quality guy. The man or woman who buys one item that lasts ten years rather than ten inferior items that will each last six months. Quality people are exactly that, quality. They think long and hard about what they want before they buy it. They know exactly what they are getting at the best price. They ask themselves: Will this item last? Will it do what it says it will? Do I really need it? Is there a better alternative? Will it make my life better? Is this another thing destroying the environment?

There are many areas where buying cheap and cheerful (aka 'quantity') is almost the norm but can end up being costly and sad. Typical areas where ignoring quality can have unpleasant consequences include food and drinks (think fake vodka, over-sugared food, even horse filled salami), motorbike helmets, inflatable boats, car tyres, all safety equipment, even mundane things like mattresses, sun cream, computers, winter wear, and boots. Rich or poor, if you buy trash, you get trash results.

One good way of seeing if you are a quantity or quality guy is to check your kitchen drawer. If there are dozens of knives, but none are sharp, you just got your answer.

Impact: Saves the world from ten purchases when one might be better.
Difficulty: Hard for the spontaneous.
Money-saving: Yes £1000+
Action: Think quality, not quantity, when making purchases.

I Do This Already ★ **I Choose This Task** ☐

Recycle Less

The metro area population of Chicago is 9.6 million people and the City of Chicago regularly hits over 50 million tourists each year. Big numbers, but it is doubtful there would be a majority of these people who know correctly what building is at 330 North Wabash Avenue in the city. Today, it is known as AMA Plaza, but it has also been the IBM Plaza, and originally the IBM Building. Ironically, for such an oft-renamed structure, the building's design, a simplistic glass and steel skyscraper, came from the German-born architect, Ludwig Mies van der Rohe, in an aesthetic style he named 'Less is more'.

Obviously, 'Less is more' when talking minimalist skyscraper is good, but 'More is more' is plain confusing when talking names. And while you're in Chicago, don't even try to find Weeghman Park (now Wrigley Field), Wanda Vista (now St Regis Chicago), Comiskey Park (now Guaranteed Rate Field), Standard Oil Building (now Aon Center), the Associates Building (now Crain Communications Building), or even Sears Tower and John Hancock Center, now Willis Tower and 875 North Michigan Avenue.

Does nothing last?

The idea of 'less is more' is not unique to the architect Ludwig Mies van der Rohe, who was also the last director of Germany's famous Bauhaus school of modern art. Indeed, the iconic French fashion designer, Coco Chanel, is noted as using a similar message in her famous quote 'Before you leave the house, look in the mirror, and take one thing off'. The earliest reference to the saying is a Robert Browning poem from 1855 entitled 'Andrea del Sarto'.

In our consume all world, the idea of 'Less is more' is a concept that is making a comeback. Think about it. Less spending equals more saving. Less talking equals more listening. Less driving equals more walking/cycling, and less stuff equals more space. The time for less is now.

One very important 'Less is more' thing people can do is recycle less.

Yep, you read that correctly. Even though the world constantly goes on about recycling, in actuality, the less we recycle at all - the better.

But why recycle less? Well, we need to first bear in mind that in 2018 the Royal Statistical Society announced the 'statistic of the year' was that 90.5% of all plastic waste has never been recycled. You read that correctly again!

The reason we recycle in the first place is because back in the day we started to have too much waste at the same time as marketeers and product makers realised consumers wanted glitzy products and easy lifestyles. People would pay more for small products if they were in big and colourful packaging. Marketeers also assumed people did not want to take stuff back to shops to refill or get deposits back on glass bottles, so along came trillions of single-use items, pull top cans, and more plastic, especially of the bottles and bags variety.

Sadly, instead of hitting the problem head on, society literally kicked the can down the road, and the idea of recycling emerged, creating the illusion that we could have it all and nothing would go to waste.

The theory was great, the practice dreadful (with some noticeable successes like Germany's bottle deposit scheme). Most 'recycling' now ends up being burnt or buried, or exported and dumped, or worse, finds its way into our land, rivers, and oceans causing incredible destruction. Recycling is not a bad idea - just a badly implemented and overused system. With effort, most people could probably get by without using most 'recyclable' items.

It might be best if we try not to get in a position where we have to recycle anything at all. The simplest way, is by becoming non-buyers of anything with packaging that is not biodegradable, edible, reusable, or returnable.

Impact: Massive reduction in ocean-bound micro plastics.
Difficulty: Hard.
Money-saving: Yes £300+
Action: Avoid using over packaged products that need recycling.

I Do This Already ★ I Choose This Task ☐

Love that Car Wash

If you take a visit to YouTube there is a video from 27 July 1973 of an American singer called Jim Croce on a BBC TV music show called *The Old Grey Whistle Test* singing a song entitled 'Working At The Car Wash Blues'. The singer is at the pinnacle of his career, having just had a number one in the USA with a song called 'Bad, Bad Leroy Brown'. Relaxed, smiling, in good voice, and obviously happy with his lot. He made many UK fans that night. Little did anyone know that a mere 55 days later he would die in a plane crash in Louisiana - and people who had never heard of him just 56 days earlier would be crying at the loss of such a charismatic singer.

The reason this is mentioned is not solely that Jim Croce was yet another tragic loss of such great musical talent taken well before their time, and needs to be remembered, but that the BBC event is probably the first ever live recording of any song about a car wash.

In subsequent years Bruce Springsteen, Randy Newman, Paul Simon and Sheryl Crow have all sung about car washes, However, the greatest homage to the car wash comes from the band Rose Royce, whose lead singer Gwen Dickey had everyone upbeat and happy in 1976 as she sang the song 'Car Wash' with its classic line: '*You might not ever get rich, but let me tell ya it's better than diggin' a ditch ... at the car wash, workin' at the car wash girl*'.

Such an optimistic disco tune, it was in the Top Twenty in at least a dozen countries and No.1 in the USA and Canada. The same Norman Whitfield penned song found massive international fame yet again, this time in 2004, when it was sung by Christina Aguilera and Missy Elliott and used on the soundtrack for the Dreamworks computer animated blockbuster, *Shark Tale*.

Seems we all love car washes, and so we should, they can help the planet!

Since Henry Ford created the first mass produced car, the Model T, in 1908, cars have needed cleaning. Early car cleaning systems included the so-called 'Automated Laundry', which saw cars pushed through an enclosed area and hand washed by people with buckets and cloths. It was not until 1951 that the first truly automated system arrived, when the three Anderson Brothers, Archie, Dean and Eldon, opened a car wash in Seattle that pulled a car along a track where machines soaped, brushed, rinsed and dried the vehicle.

Whatever system was used, automated, or hand washed, most of the history of car washing has involved harsh soaps and chemicals that can result in polluted cleaning water that includes phosphates, detergents, surfactants, oils, silts, rubber, and metals, discharging into the ground or sewers.

In recent years, the environmental problems of runoff from washing cars has become a major issue. Some car makers have tried to address the problem at source, such as Nissan, who prototyped self-cleaning cars by introducing car paint that repelled mud and dirt, so required much less cleaning. Improved, and supposedly more eco-friendly cleaning products have been introduced by the cleaning products industry, while many governments have regulated the car wash industry to include, sludge pits, oil interceptors, and to ensure all run-off is treated. The car wash industry itself has also introduced water recycling systems. Some countries, like Germany, have even made it illegal to wash your car on your driveway, thus forcing the use of highly regulated car cleaning establishments.

If you want to help the environment, then the next time you wash your car, make sure your only run-off is the run off to the car wash!

It's better than diggin' a ditch!

Impact: Safe disposal of polluted runoff from up to 1.4 billion vehicles.
Difficulty: Super easy.
Money-saving: No.
Action: Get car dirty. Take to car wash (on route somewhere else). Clean car.

I Do This Already  **I Choose This Task**

Halve Your Mileage

History is chock-full of some magnificent national leaders. Men and women who cared for their people and fought tirelessly on their behalf, sometimes under great stress and difficult circumstances. Think, Mahatma Gandhi, Alexander the Great, Joan of Arc, Nelson Mandela, Winston Churchill, Queen Victoria, George Washington, Maharaja Ranjit Singh, Queen Elizabeth I, Catherine the Great, Oda Nobunaga, Asoka, Simon Bolivar, Abraham Lincoln, etc.

As recent events have most certainly highlighted, many of the Monarchs, Presidents, and Prime Ministers of today will struggle to edge their way into history's list of great leaders. That said, one sure way they could collectively open the door to membership of this esteemed group, would be to decide to instantly save the lives of around 675,000 people in the world this year alone and stop up to 25 million others from being injured. At the same time having a massive impact on the environment by reducing CO2 emissions in places like North America and Europe by over 15%.

They could do this by persuading their citizens to drive their cars just half their normal mileage. In an instant the world would change. A lot less traffic jams, easier commutes, kids walking or cycling rather than being forced onto hassle-filled school runs every day, half the road rage incidents, easier parking if you do drive somewhere, better public transport services funded by increased demand, more money in everyone's pockets, and, of course, a lot less deaths and non-fatal injuries caused from road accidents.

Few leaders of today are going to even suggest this. But you, all by yourself, could half any possible road deaths or injuries you may be involved in - plus reduce your car emissions by 50% - by making a one second decision to go one year driving half the miles you normally would.

Similar-ish ideas are already being tried in various world locations. These are mostly by means of road rationing such as creating road restrictions as used at all recent Olympic Games, no-drive days like those in Beijing during high pollution periods, alternate day driving such as that in Sao Paulo, Brazil, and car emission tolls like London's ULEZ scheme. Often, they work well, but in some cases people use loopholes or money to evade the schemes. Jakarta, for example, allowed car pools to use priority lanes but abandoned this after drivers began hiring people, known as car jockeys, to drive with them so it looked like a car pool. This was replaced by a number plate system, with odd number cars using roads one day, and even numbers the next. Some drivers beat the system by buying second cars with opposing number plates. If only this ingenuity could be used to solve problems not skate around them.

To halve your personal mileage, first check your figure for last year. Information that, dependent on where you live, can be found on insurance documents, vehicle inspection papers, or your service book. If you are in the US, the average person drives 13,500 miles, while in the UK the average car drives 6,800 miles, but everyone is unique. Once you have your annual figure, say the EU average of 7,500 miles, then halve it (3,750), then split that figure by 52 to know how many miles you can allow yourself (72 miles) to drive each week. Try to keep below that weekly amount so you can save miles for bigger drives you know are coming up (like holidays). The amount of fuel you will save, reduced maintenance, lower insurance cost, and better sale price of your lower mileage car, should make a significant boost to your finances.

If they could talk, both the environment, and those who are no longer destined to die or be injured in a car accident would surely say, 'thank you'.

Impact: Reduce vehicle CO2 emissions in parts of the world by up to 15%.
Difficulty: Moderate to hard.
Money-saving: Yes £1000+
Action: Make decision to halve mileage. Do it.

I Do This Already ★ I Choose This Task ☐

Go Meat Minor

There are some topics that are just so emotive, so subjective, and so delicate to discuss in polite company that it is normally wise to stay well away from them unless you truly enjoy a debate, are happy alienating people, losing friends, or worse, gaining friends who only want to be your friend because they like to argue. We all know the topics that can make people feel like they are walking on eggshells: sex, politics, religion, money, and of course, football. And don't ever mention Trump or Brexit or masks or abortion or immigration or trans rights or Marmite! As Twitter has made very clear, we have all got a view.

One such subject today is that of veganism. The saviour of the planet in the minds of some, the destruction of the known world to others.

Will we really be such massive consumers of meat 1000 years from now as we are today? It is doubtful, but we can never second guess the future. In the Douglas Adams TV series *The Hitchhiker's Guide To The Galaxy* the main character, Arthur Dent, finds himself at a place called Milliways, the restaurant 'At The End Of The Universe'. When the waiter shows them the 'dish of the day' they discover a live animal on a trolley, the Ameglian Major Cow, a talking cow that wants to be eaten. The cow actively promotes the parts of its body it has worked on to get the best taste, such as its rump and liver. Arthur Dent, disgusted at the thought, makes plain to his fellow guests, 'I don't want to eat an animal that's lying there inviting me to eat it', only for it to be pointed out to him that surely, 'It's better than eating an animal that doesn't want to be eaten'.

Whatever your view on meat, whether from a culinary, traditionalist, ethical, cultural, religious, or health perspective, we can all understand that society's over emphasis on this one food source has a big effect on the environment.

The Food and Agriculture Organization of the United Nations (FAO) state that the world's livestock represent 14.5 percent of all 'anthropogenic greenhouse gas emissions'. In normal-speak, this essentially means that our keeping of animals for food and milk is causing roughly one-seventh of all the climate changing gas emissions caused by human activities. This is serious.

Today, around 88% of the world's population are classed as meat eaters. Most love their burgers, bacon, pork or chicken way too much to end that relationship. That said, there is a swing to a vegan-ish lifestyle, helped by the development and sale of plant-based, 'meat-free-meats'. There are even meat alternatives being developed, originating from NASA space food projects, that literally convert elements in the air, such as carbon dioxide, into 'meat' using microbes known as hydrogenotrophs. Cool!

This book is not suggesting you should go all Paul McCartney, Miley Cyrus, Woody Harrelson, Ellen DeGeneres, or Bill Clinton, and stop eating meat. That's something your medical doctor, or your purse, or your personal beliefs, need to work out. However, for the sake of the environment, it might be a very good thing to consider going 'meat minor'. Simply cutting back from having a diet that includes meat on every plate. This isn't some new fad idea, indeed, long before Meatless Mondays there was Pres Woodrow Wilson's Meatless Days during World War One and Pres Truman's post-World War Two 'Meatless Tuesday' and 'Poultryless Thursday' campaigns.

As a complete aside, the Thanksgiving tradition of giving a Turkey to the US President began as a subtle protest by lobbyists against Poultryless Thursday in 1947 - but instead of now being about eating more meat, by the 1970s it had morphed into the President not eating the bird but pardoning it.

Impact: Eating 50% less meat saves 7% of all greenhouse gas emissions.
Difficulty: Sounds hard, but is actually quite easy.
Money-saving: Yes £100+
Action: Change diet to halve amount of meat consumed each week.

I Do This Already  **I Choose This Task** ☐

Be Illuminated by the Difference Lights Bulbs Make to the World

How many politicians does it take to change a lightbulb? One to call an election assuming they would win because everyone else was completely in the dark. One to promise a brighter tomorrow and actually win. Twenty to run a committee to discuss the problem and work out who to blame. One to tell us everything humanly possible was being done to change things. One to go out and actually buy a lightbulb. One to hold the lightbulb while 999 others try to turn the ceiling around. One to change the policy on the ceiling turning. One to then screw it in. One to check the work but end up screwing it up. And one, who used to be in PR, making everything look good by giving the end bit a new twist. So, a total of 1028 politicians.

However, this would be followed by another 1028 politicians who don't like how it was done, complain it cost too much, don't like the new bulb, and want to change it back to how it used to be in 'the good old days'.

Nowhere in this would there be any mention of lighting technicians, building supervisors, janitors, or straightforward 'can do' types, who, even though they 'don't like the spotlight' would have changed the bulb in seconds.

You would also hear no mention of environmentalists or the world's scientific community. The environmentalists would be in hospital - all having burnt their fingers trying to change the bulb when it wasn't cool enough to do so.

The scientists would simply have pointed out that the bulb never stopped working in the first place. It was a long-lasting low-energy LED bulb, and the politicians simply failed to notice the light switch wasn't turned on.

The lights are on, but is anyone home?

The first house in the world to be lit by electric light bulbs was Underhill House, 99 Kells Lane, Gateshead, England, on 3 February 1879. It belonged to physicist, Joseph Swan, who had created the first practical incandescent electric lamp. It wasn't long before Swan and American inventor Thomas Edison, who was also working on electric light bulbs, joined forces to create the Edison and Swan United Electric Light Company.

The advent of stable light in homes was an absolute game changer. The ability to see clearly in the evenings, night, and early mornings without being choked out by gas flames transformed day-to-day (or more night-to-night) life in an instant.

In the fourteen decades that followed, the light bulb had minor changes but was still shamefully energy inefficient, converting only 5% of the electricity they used into light. They also didn't last too long, purposely held back to become obsolete after roughly 1,000 hours. Amazingly, people still use them.

The big change came in 1962 when Nick Holonyak Jr invented the first visible-light Light Emitting Diode (LED). This led to the development of today's modern LED light bulbs, which became commercially available 40 years later in 2002. Today they are everywhere - and cheap - and they use around 75% less energy than incandescent bulbs - and last 25 times longer.

In the USA the percentage of home electricity used on lighting, according to the US Energy Information Administration (EIA) is 4%, down from 10% six years ago. In major part, this is down to new LED bulbs.

Making use of the most energy efficient LED bulbs plays a part in energy (and money) saving in the home, but this can be added to with motion sensors on lights (especially outdoor lights), not using so many lamps in one room, or simply turning off lights when you are not using them.

Impact: Reduction of up to 6% of electricity needed in the home.
Difficulty: Easy.
Money-saving: Yes £100+
Action: Change old bulbs for LED.

I Do This Already  **I Choose This Task**

eBill and eTicket Whenever You Can

The International Civil Aviation Organization (ICAO) reported that in the year before the global pandemic some 4.5 billion passengers had been carried on the world's airlines. That incredible figure equates to literally every person in Australia, all 26 million of them, taking 305 flights every year.

Officially, airline paper tickets were replaced by e-tickets a long time ago (May 2008) but the decision to print them out ourselves at home or in the office, or use our phones as the ticket, has been left, mostly, to the individual. Every airline is different so when people go to print their actual flight ticket they can either get one page of A4 paper or up to what feels like a 100 pages filled with extra information and upsell adverts.

If every air-traveller printed just the main page of their e-ticket before travel that would equate to 4.5 billion A4 sheets. There are many variables at play as to how many sheets of A4 paper can be made from a typical tree, such as density of wood, thickness of tree, height of tree, etc., but the general figure is 10,000 sheets per tree (or just 20 reams). This means in one year we could use 450,000 trees - simply to get on planes.

And this is just today. In an interview with TV economist Jim Cramer in 2017 the former CEO of Boeing, Dennis Muilenburg, noted that less than 20% of the world's population has ever taken a flight.

If the printed ticket paper is from sustainable sources this is not such a big deal, but is a good example of how small things that could be done digitally can add up to real world consequences. That said, for anyone with an e-ticket who has lost power on their phone .... well, that's another story.

E-tickets, e-billing, and a paperless world are now the norm. If possible use them wherever you can, especially if there is a financial incentive to do so.

The paperless world is everywhere. No more physical bus tickets, train tickets, theatre tickets, car park tickets, membership cards, bank and credit card statements, physical letter confirmations, and utility bills. Even paper money has taken a hit as it seemed the whole world went from using paper money to contactless/tap-and-go cards in the space of a few weeks when the Covid-19 pandemic took hold in early 2020.

A survey by MasterCard at the start of the pandemic showed that 79% of people around the world and 91% of people in the Asia-Pacific region were using contactless/tap-and-go payments. The main reason given at the time was safety and cleanliness, things which still apply today. You could also add ease and speed of use, and more importantly, the benefit to the environment of using one plastic/metal card or phone screen as payment instead of thousands of well touched and well used bits of paper/plastic notes.

One very interesting benefit of going paperless is that it could possibly allow you up to five months extra free time in life. This is because, according to research carried out for one of the main insurance companies in the UK, the average person will spend a total of 153 days of their life looking for lost items. Mostly, this is mundane stuff like the TV remote, glasses, toys, underwear, etc. but also includes paperwork, tickets, diaries and organisers. Tagging physical stuff with a locator linked to your phone would certainly help get some of that time back, as would the use of e-tickets, e-billing, and all paperless documentation. Unless, of course, you lose your phone or laptop.

Going paperless in life has many benefits including ease of access, ability to quickly share information, reduced stationery and storage costs, even plain cleanliness. But mostly, it simply helps reduce our impact on the environment.

Impact: Considerable reduction in non sustainably-managed forestry.
Difficulty: Easy.
Money-saving: Yes £10+
Action: Adopt eticketing and ebilling wherever possible.

Double Offset Your Carbon Footprint

Only on planet Earth could the idea of carbon offsetting exist. Essentially an accounting system used to allow companies and individuals to pollute the planet, but then pay someone else to not pollute the planet by the same amount, or to do something that removes the same amount of pollution.

This may seem, as former US President Obama once described climate deniers, 'cray cray' (check your urban dictionary, but you can probably guess), but it is absolutely real. Indeed, the carbon offset market is worth $1 billion a year and expected to rise to a truly scary $150 billion a year by 2030.

Carbon offsetting, as we know it right now, is quite simply the buying and selling of non-pollution by polluters - and a very useful way for less environment friendly companies and organisations to do something called 'greenwashing' (make something look environment friendly when in reality it is absolutely not).

The concept is quite bizarre and it is amusing to wonder if other things could also be 'offset'. How popular do you think a 'Crime Offsetting' scheme might be if made available to companies and the public? You simply commit the crime, say rob a bank, then pay a quarter or half the amount to a much poorer criminal in a poorer part of the world to come forward and admit to the crime and do the jail time, or they promise not to rob a bank for a set period of time in their part of the world - and everything is yin-yang good.

Similarly, how about 'Affair Offsetting', where a husband or wife can be seen publicly having 'sexy time' with someone (or everyone) other than their spouse. But, hand on heart, claim everything is OK because a sex worker in Amsterdam had been paid to not participate in their chosen career for a few days to redress the balance.

Joking aside, in the real world, there is a place for some modest system of carbon offsetting. One that is part of a globally regulated organisation. A body that measures 'real' things that companies or individuals are doing to improve the environment, before allowing trades in the carbon offsetting market.

This doesn't presently exist. So once again, it is down to the individuals of the world to sort things out. The first way is find out how any company you have dealings with is working to reduce climate change. If they are totally reliant on carbon offsetting, they are not actually helping at all. They are just paying to not have the problem. Worse, they are using your money to do so. One way of showing your displeasure at this is by moving over to any of their competitors that are doing something real to beat climate change.

The second thing people can do is to 'double offset' themselves - essentially work out their own carbon footprint - either for their general presence here in life, or on a particular thing or event, like taking an international flight or driving a fossil-fuel car. The person, with a figure for their carbon footprint then offsets the amount for the thing itself - but then offsets again (double offsets), to make up for their impact on the planet going back in time - retrospectively. Essentially a 'do one bad', 'pay two good' situation.

People can use offsetting organisations that already exist, such as many wildlife and forestry charities that have specific projects, but you can also invest your double offset cash in companies that are actively creating carbon neutral solutions such as renewable energy companies or EV makers.

In practice 'double offsetting' doesn't just pay to balance out the carbon you create. It also counteracts what you've already done in the past - and acts as an anchor to making better decisions about 'ungreen' things you do now.

Impact: You still pollute, but make up for it by double stopping the same amount of pollution elsewhere.
Difficulty: Easy. Probably too easy.
Money-saving: No.
Action: Most environment charities have carbon offsetting schemes, or invest offsetting funds into green businesses.

I Choose This Task ☐

Become Minimalist and Bring Out Your Inner Spartan

If you've ever seen the 2006 film *300*, starring Gerard Butler, Michael Fassbinder, and Lena Headey, you will be aware of the Battle of Thermopylae, fought in 480BC, between an alliance of Greek City States against the might of the Persian Empire, whose army numbered one million (or 150,000 according to modern scholars). As part of the battle, the Greeks sent 7,000 men to defend a narrow coastal pass at Thermopylae where the massive Persian forces would try to pass through. A force of 300 Spartan soldiers led by King Leonidas I blocked the pass for a week, and legend suggests that after three days of non-stop fighting, the Persian's so-called 'Immortals' had lost 20,000 men. Betrayed by a shepherd who guided the Persians around the site, the Spartans then fought both ends of the pass to their last man. The Greeks lost the battle but, inspired by Spartan bravery, eventually won the war.

In the aftermath of the battle the legend of Spartan warrior prowess grew to such an extent that many other nations (including the mighty Roman Empire) tried to emulate much of what they believed made the Spartans so effective. They understood Spartans to be completely self-reliant and able as individuals, yet also able to work effectively as part of one unit in battle. They believed Spartan soldiers were trained from childhood and, unlike other armies, were full-time fighters. Their whole life and sole profession being that of a warrior. Spartans maximised their scouts to ensure they had advance information on their enemy's position and the best knowledge on where, or if, to fight. They were also able to communicate well in the heat of battle, always followed orders, and never gave up. Above all they were fit, strong, swift, intelligent, and had little baggage - they could live and thrive in whatever surroundings they found themselves.

If you feel inspired to do your best King Leonidas impression and scream, 'This Is Sparta!' at the top of your voice, then maybe it is time for you to make contact with your inner spartan for the benefit of today's known world. There is no need to go out fighting Persian armies or wearing leather Speedo's, big boots, and a red cape. Instead, learning minimalism and frugality, while being determined, focused and cheerful enough to make the best with what you have around you, is a great start.

Many of the world's richest people, famous celebs, even national leaders exemplify many aspects of Spartan living. Warren Buffett still drives his old 2014 Cadillac XTS, even though he has given away to charity some $34 billion - enough to buy a brand new Bentley Continental GT V8 convertible every year for the next 152,671 years. World famous singer Ed Sheeran, who is worth around £220 million ($300m), is reported to give himself a personal allowance of just £1000 ($1350) a month. Former Uruguay President Jose Mujica, styled as the 'humblest head of state in the world' when he was leader, gave 90% of his salary to charity.

The virtues of thrift, frugality, and minimalism are good for the environment because, essentially, they don't waste valuable resources. Of course, being Spartan in nature doesn't mean you will never be rich. It simply means you don't need to be rich in the first place, and can focus more on your actual role in life, which, coincidentally, is one of the things that creates wealth. Who knew?

There are minimalism groups everywhere, so there is no excuse about not knowing how to do more with less. Who really needs four homes, seventy-four designer handbags, three cars, and 105 pairs of shoes? Yes, remember Sparta, but never forget that minimalism is a good friend of a happy life.

Impact: Minimalism saves valuable resources.
Difficulty: Very hard for most people.
Money-saving: Yes £100+
Action: Join minimalism group or employ aspects of minimalism in your life.

I Do This Already  **I Choose This Task**

Boot Sales, Auctions, Selling Sites and Charity Shops Get a Classified Education

In February 2015, the US Marshall Service held an auction via Gaston & Sheehan Auctioneers of Pflugerville (great name), Texas. One of the online bidders to the auction was a lady called Nancy Carlson of Inverness, Illinois. She had taken interest in a 'lunar sample return bag' and ended up bidding $995. Just two years later that same bag, by now verified as having been used by Neil Armstrong to collect samples from the Moon, and having some dust left in the bag, was up for auction at Sotheby's. It sold for $1.8 million.

In 2013, on the BBC 'Antiques Roadshow' programme, a priest brought along an old painting he had bought for £400 from an antique shop in the lovely English town of Nantwich in Cheshire. He liked the golden frame and was amazed to discover the painting was an original Van Dyck worth £400,000.

In March 2021, a rare 15th century porcelain bowl from China was sold at Sotheby's for $722,000. It was from the period of the Yongle Emperor in the Ming Dynasty and only six other similar bowls are known to exist in the world. The seller had acquired the bowl at a yard sale in Connecticut for the bargain price of $35.

In April 2014, 300 students at the University of Brighton in England completed 'The Waste House', a large low-energy building that was 85% made using waste, junk, and unwanted materials. Stuff that would otherwise be thrown away. Many of the materials were sourced free online.

Whether online classifieds, yard sales, flea markets, antique shops, auctions, free sites, or charity shops, there is a whole world of low cost, even free, items available, that have value and purpose - and don't cost the planet.

Thinking of getting some new furniture? What about a new TV? Maybe a new door, or a vase, or a laptop, or phone, or desk, or a rug, or a pan, or a book, or a million and one other possible purchases? Are you ready to nip out to your local store or go online to buy them brand new, right now?

If so ... STOP! Just back off the 'new' idea for now, and at the same time the 'full price' idea, and see if you can get the same, or almost the same item, or an even better item, second-hand (or pre-owned, pre-loved, used, nearly new, unwanted, free, antique, reclaimed, classic, vintage or any other 'not new' title).

There are literally thousands of people around the world who have filled their homes with high quality items, useful to them, for a fraction of the price or even free - and have the satisfaction of knowing they are helping the environment by doing so. Some have built whole kitchens complete with appliances, re-styled their homes, even built a whole house from being able to understand the world of classified ads, the second-hand or freecycle websites or physical boot sales, flea markets, or charity shops.

A new car, traditionally loses 10% of its value the instant it is driven off the forecourt, while the average car may have lost over half its value in just three years. Surely, the smarter money suggests not buying a new car at all, and instead buying a car that is one month old - or three years old.

Most people think in terms of 'old or new', but it might be wiser to ignore age and instead think 'quality or trash' when buying items.

Learning how to use local item re-distribution websites, like eBay, craigslist, gumtree, pre-loved, shpock, loot, etc., are a good means of seeing if you can get the items you need (not want). They are also useful for another purpose, donating or selling stuff you yourself no longer want or can use.

Impact: Makes use of supposed waste or items others don't want.
Difficulty: Easy.
Money-saving: Yes. Up to £1.8m!
Action: Explore the world of sales websites, auctions and classified ads.

I Choose This Task ☐

Gym No
Outdoor Fitness Yes

There's a really odd fact that most people should remember when they think about whether they are devoting enough time to their fitness. In the UK the average person spends twice as much time on the toilet than they do being physically active. Yep, 3 hours and 9 minutes is the amount of time the average Brit spends in the smallest room each week compared to 1 hour 30 minutes of exercise. Now, before everyone starts laughing at visions of Mr Bean, James Bond, Harry Potter, or Queen Elizabeth II sat doing their 'throne time' instead of their fitness time, it might be worth pointing out these are not too dissimilar figures to most other Western countries. In fact, according to the Centers for Disease Control (CDC) only 22.9% of all adults in the USA do the recommended amount of physical activity.

Fitness is important, but the way in which we stay fit and healthy is also crucial and can make a big difference to our impact on the planet.

One of the more amazing sights seen in the vicinity of most gyms is the size of their car parks. Seriously, just satellite map your local gym or health club and look at the footprint of their building compared to the footprint of the car park. Time after time the car park tends to be bigger than the building. These locations are supposedly all about health and fitness, yet facilitate the majority of their customers to drive a car the couple of miles or so from their homes to its premises (most gym users live within four miles of their regular gym). This doesn't make sense, especially when the customers then get out of their cars and start running on treadmills. If it's never been said before, it should be now: 'Sparta never had car parks'.

If you want to join a gym or fitness group, maybe it's time to start using an outdoor one, or using the outdoors itself as the gym or fitness location.

Outdoor gyms, such as the type found in local parks or in the grounds of sports centres tend to be free or have minimal fees. Some of the more impressive outdoor gyms even have high quality running or walking tracks around their edges - or screens from which trainers run classes. Many pieces of gym equipment in the most impressive of outdoor gyms can even link to your phone/ smart tech and show your personal exercise data.

Indoor gyms are built to help people get fit and healthier, and is something the 180 million gym members worldwide would agree they most certainly accomplish. However, unless thoroughly and regularly cleaned and having fantastic HVAC (heating, ventilation and air conditioning) systems, they are also prone to being home to harmful bacteria on the equipment itself and have high levels of indoor air pollution.

Given the choice between exercising 'indoors' or 'in nature' there are few who would not recommend the latter. Indoor gyms literally remove people from the healthier environment of the natural world whether it be a garden, local park, or a nearby forest or wilderness area.

Exercise and the environment have always gone hand in hand from hunter gatherers running, throwing, swimming, and carrying to get meat and fish, to farmers clearing and toiling the land to grow fruit, vegetables, and cereals.

Want a 'good for the environment' work out? Stuff the gym. Walk, run, or cycle to work, start a veg/fruit garden, volunteer for outdoor or heavy work, and use the money saved, plus use the average £400 a year gym membership fee, to do something green - like buy some trees or invest in wind or solar, or even an outdoor gym company.

Impact: Small but positive impact on the environment. Good for individuals.
Difficulty: Easy to start, hard to maintain.
Money-saving: Yes £400+
Action: Don't join a gym. Start exercising outdoors in nature or using an outdoor gym.

I Choose This Task

Invest in Your Bill Makers

Many people reading this will never have heard the name Victor Kiam, but for a long period throughout the 1980s, the New Orleans born salesman was seen on TV ads all around the world showing off his Remington Electric Shaver. One of the lines used in the TV commercial was 'I liked the shaver so much - I bought the company'.

It was true, Victor Kiam had indeed recently purchased the Remington brand under a leveraged buyout for $25 million and was now the boss of what had been a loss making company. The TV advert, with its notion of the owner putting his money where his mouth was, resonated well with the public and sales went through the roof. Remington went from losses of $30 million in the three years before his purchase to immediate profit.

Victor Kiam was a one man business whirlwind and went on to own the New England Patriots, but none of his great wealth would have been possible had he not been confident enough to invest in something he understood personally to be of value. He already used a Remington shaver in his day to day life and he personally loved the product more than anything else on the market at the time.

In investment terms, the idea of putting money into something you already understand is a solid principle. In 'enconomy' terms (the environmental economy), the idea of putting money in the environment friendly companies you already use, respect, and can see have a future, is just plain sensible.

If Victor Kiam was alive today, it would be nice to think he would power his electric shaver with renewable energy. If he did, it would not be too much of a stretch of the imagination to think instead of just paying his electricity bill, he would also invest or end up owning that same electric company.

As individuals, we all make thousands of decisions each year as to who and where we want our money to go. If you buy a Mars Bar from Tesco, your money goes to those two companies and via them to hundreds of other businesses from advertising agencies to dairy and cocoa farmers, to wrapper makers and designers, haulage firms, security contractors, etc. Most of our decisions are quite small, but some, like who to choose as your electricity supplier, or model of car you want to drive, can involve large sums of money. Whatever the purchase decision, big or small, they all have consequences.

If you have considered the implications of your major purchases with a mind to the environment, are happy or excited with your purchase decisions, and feel super content about your relationship with your seller/supplier and their product, then perhaps you've just done most of the homework to do one extra thing with them. Collaborate.

The idea of collaborating with those who take your money may seem strange, but if you think about it - you actively chose them over their competition, and you are the future. You are the environmentally aware consumer.

Collaboration doesn't mean wearing their corporate clothes or going to their Christmas parties, but simply means investing in what they do.

If you've reduced your electricity bill by changing your energy habits then why not use that saving to invest in the company who supply your renewable electricity. If you have bought an electric car and love it, why not invest the savings in fuel costs with the car maker.

These companies are taking your money, and if you are happy with what they are doing with it and the service/product they supply - why not get some of that money back as dividends from what they keep doing well!

Impact: Renewable or green industry investment is great for the planet.
Difficulty: Easy.
Money-saving: Yes-No-Maybe.
Action: Invest any green savings you make into environment-minded companies.

I Choose This Task

Cleaning Your Home Should Not Dirty the Planet

Few people would ever assume that a small child dropping a toy and too much paper in the toilet could end up with firefighters cordoning off a street while they dealt with a life-threatening chemical incident, but that is exactly what happened in December 2018 in the small town of Nailsea in Somerset, England. The child's mother tried to clear the clogged toilet with two bottles of a branded toilet unblocker and a large container of bleach, but the two products reacted to create large quantities of deadly chlorine gas, the same chemical that is banned for use as a weapon by the Geneva Convention. Thankfully, the family quickly exited the house, the firefighters cleared the fumes, and all ended well (except no one got to bed until 5am).

This type of incident, as many firefighters will tell you, is not uncommon, and doesn't always have a happy ending. Just a year later, in Burlington, Massachusetts, two different cleaning products were accidentally mixed while a restaurant kitchen floor was being cleaned. The reaction caused toxic fumes which ended with a dozen people going to hospital and the manager of the restaurant losing his life.

Cleaning products are serious things, and if not used correctly with proper regard to health and safety can have serious effects on the human body - most notably their ingredients reacting badly with the eyes, skin, or respiratory system. Many of these same cleaning products can also have a major impact on the environment. The ingredients of some cleaning products can bypass water treatment plants and end up in our rivers, lakes, and oceans where they can affect the water system, wildlife, and plants - and enter our food chain.

Cleaning is a super necessary part of life, but we don't need to pollute to be clean.

If you have ever found yourself emptying a vacuum cleaner into a wheelie bin on a windy day, kneeling down in a shower to clean a plughole, or trying to scrub some weird unknown stain on a rug - then you have probably wondered what would happen if you just stopped cleaning and left it all to nature.

Sadly, within a few days things would begin to get ... gross. The increase in dust (of which roughly a third is made from dead skin) would fill your home with dust mites - and allergies. Those dropped crumbs, not cleaned up, would attract flies, ants, cockroaches, even rodents (and the horrible illnesses they can share). Your bed would be a mix of literally everything that has been on you - plus dust mites, and their not so lovely micro faeces. The bathroom would become a moist biohazard. The dirt and mould in your fridge may end up poisoning you. You will most likely stink - and soon notice you have fewer and fewer people coming around for coffee and cake.

Clean is good, and there are a number of things people can do to eradicate or minimise the impact of their cleaning regime on the environment. The simplest is to look at using more natural and sustainable alternatives in cleaning products, such as vinegar or lemon, pine oils, even solvents made from seeds and vegetables. Reading and understanding what ingredients make up your cleaning products is also vital. If these have high Volatile Organic Compounds (VOCs), which can affect the respiratory system, do you really want to use them? Knowledge is safety.

The packaging for your cleaning products is also important, pump sprays are better than aerosols, and refillable containers beat single-use ones.

Finally, store products safely. The Centers for Disease Control and Prevention (CDC) states that 374 children are poisoned each day in the USA alone.

Impact: Reduces pollution which might otherwise get into our food chain.
Difficulty: Medium. Needs research.
Money-saving: No.
Action: Check all your cleaning products and research more natural alternatives.

I Do This Already ★ I Choose This Task

Think Before You Buy

One of the greatest ever football players in the history of the game was a young Northern Irishman called George Best, who played for Manchester United from 1963 to 1974. Friendly, funny, photogenic, exciting, and naturally gifted as a footballer, his fellow footballers, the fans, the public, even the notoriously tough British newspapers loved him. Nicknamed 'the Fifth Beatle', he epitomised the Swinging Sixties. He owned trendy night clubs, fashion boutiques, and was never short of female company. His fame went beyond the game and he is regarded as one of the first male superstar sex symbols in sport. Best's later career took him around the world as a player for LA Aztecs, San Jose Earthquakes, Fort Lauderdale Strikers, Hong Kong Rangers and the Brisbane Lions. The hard-drinking sportsman was reported to have had affairs with seven Miss Worlds - something he later clarified as incorrect, stating it was only four! He lived a big life, his star was bright, and when he died in 2005, aged 59, from alcohol-related illness, he left only £136,000 in his will. He had spent millions.

The reason Best is mentioned here is simple, when asked about his big spending, he is famously quoted as saying 'I spent a lot of money on booze, birds (women), and fast cars. The rest I just squandered'.

We're sure that today, Best's fast cars would all be electric, the booze all organic and from sustainable sources, and his love life conducted under very eco-friendly conditions. And if millionaire sports stars don't like squandering money, then that's a message we should all take to heart.

Most of us are like George. We love to spend, spend, spend. All the environment and future generations ask is that when you do, you think about any climate changing effects of your purchase before you do so.

There is a common saying that the two best days of owning a holiday home are the day you buy it - and the day you sell it!

True or not, it's funny, and is a nice lead to why people should seriously think about every purchase they ever make. Not just the big ticket stuff like holiday homes, boats, sports cars, computers and the like, but everything, from a chocolate bar to an avocado - or even trendy nightclubs and fashionable boutiques.

Most people, in the developed world, do not have enough savings to pay their bills beyond three months if they lost their jobs. They are literally 13 'unlucky' weeks away from serious money problems. At the same time most people, though not living exactly hand to mouth, are happy to live lives that think money is lava and will burn our wallets/purses/pockets if we don't spend it quickly. The upshot is that masses of the Earth's resources are unnecessarily used on not needed items so we can momentarily feel good about ourselves.

Overbuying and climate change are linked. In a bad way! While spending less and saving money is good for both the individual and the environment.

One way to reduce unneeded spending is to employ the idea of '***Walk, Sort, Thought***', and '***Good, Green, Mean***' when you want to buy something. This works by first ***walk***ing back from any purchase, leaving it until the next day so there is no spontaneous purchase. You then ***sort*** what you already own to see if you have similar or an alternative. You then give ***thought*** to whether you need the thing (positive) or just want it (negative). If it passes, then you only want a ***good*** one, the best. You then consider how ***green*** the item is - is it sustainable, did it travel from far away, does it wreck the place it's made, etc. The final, fun, bit is getting the ***mean***est price possible.

Every purchase has an impact somewhere - make yours few, but positive.

Impact: Saves Earth's resources from needlessly being turned into trash.
Difficulty: Easy.
Money-saving: Yes £1000+
Action: When making a purchase, don't forget: Walk, Sort, Thought and Good, Green, Mean.

I Do This Already ★ I Choose This Task ☐

Greeting Cards

Mixing quotes from US founding father Benjamin Franklin, Gone With The Wind writer Margaret Mitchell, and Robinson Crusoe author Daniel Defoe, it seems the only three certainties in life are births, deaths, and taxes - and none come at a convenient time!

There may, however, be a couple of other things that need to be added to that list. The first is that you (or more likely your relatives) will surely receive a greeting/condolence card for the first two events, whilst the second is you can absolutely guarantee that you will never receive a 'Thank You' card for the third!

Talking of births and deaths, while happily ignoring taxes, this might be a great moment to point out that another certainty in life is that coincidence is more common, and more freaky, than anyone could ever imagine. How else could it be that the brilliant theoretical physicist, Stephen Hawking, was born on the 300th anniversary of the death of Galileo (08 Jan 1942), but died on the 139th anniversary of the birth of Albert Einstein (14 Mar 2018). Three of the greatest minds this planet ever produced. All linked by greeting card moments.

Coincidence continues as we note that this same Stephen Hawking, a man born in Oxford but who died in Cambridge, spent much of his time during his later years trying to warn the world of an impending climate change 'tipping point' where global warming would become irreversible. He is sorely missed.

Getting back to greeting cards, it is worthwhile noting that this industry is big business. Indeed the US Greeting Card Association suggests Americans send around 6.5 billion greeting cards each year, while CardFactory in the UK point out to their investors that Brits sent 834 million cards in 2020.

Globally, the greeting card market is worth an estimated $23 billion - which, to put this figure into context, means every man, woman and child on the planet spends an average of $3 every year. This is considerably higher than what almost anyone on the planet spends on planting trees each year.

Greeting cards, traditionally an illustrated message used to convey a sentiment appropriate to an event or occasion, have a history going right back to the Bronze Age. Indeed, Ancient Egyptians sent greetings on papyrus scrolls.

The real initiator for the greeting card industry was St Valentine's Day, with the first known Valentine's message of love being sent in 1415 by Charles, the Duke of Orleans, to his wife in France, while he was imprisoned at the Tower of London. By the Victorian era it wasn't uncommon to send messages of love in paper, lace, or woodblock, in honour of St Valentine.

In 1843, the industry grew considerably after Sir Henry Cole, a British civil servant, hired illustrator and artist John Calcott Horsley to create a Christmas card that Cole could send to his friends and family.

Greeting cards were traditionally sent to people you were unable to greet personally. In many ways a return to this original idea combined with a more smart tech approach could be of great benefit to the environment. If you can greet someone personally, why send a card? If you can't greet someone personally it might be better, and more personable, to send a recorded video message. Something easily saved for the years ahead.

Another growing idea is to share two cards between the same two people/families that can be sent on alternate Christmases. This idea can also apply to Valentine's day, Halloween, Easter, even birthdays - of which there are around 21.5 million each day.

If you do send cards, to help the environment it is best to ensure they are from a sustainable source, are not wrapped in plastic, don't have plastic glitter on them, and aren't embossed with plastic. There is also a growing market in artisan made 3D cards, and cards embedded with seeds that can be planted after use which grow to be beautiful flowers.

TIP: Never send a glitter covered Happy Environment Day card to anyone!

Impact: Video or sustainable card is low/no CO_2 and zero plastic.
Difficulty: Easy - and fun.
Money-saving: Yes. £5+
Action: Share greeting cards or make more greeting video messages.

I Choose This Task ☐

Earth Needs Air - Not Smoke

The author of this book wants you to know something very personal, he does not smoke, would never smoke, would never want anyone he knows to smoke, and has not smoked for such a long time he probably couldn't even light a match or roll his own cigarette. He also has zero idea of how much cigarettes cost or knows what is or isn't the most popular brand. One drag of a cigarette, cigar, or pipe, and he'd be coughing for weeks.

Bizarrely, this same person, when in the company of those who do smoke, will still go outside with them to have a chat while they have their cigarette. He may no longer smoke but still vainly persists in the idea that many of the most interesting people to be met and many of the best conversations to be had, happen on the outside of the building with people who are enveloped in their blue haze of cigarette smoke. Very old habits die hard (although in contrast, actual smokers die easy).

Thankfully, most people in the western world today don't understand the previously supposed 'cool' of the smoker. They have never witnessed James Dean in 'Rebel Without a Cause', Uma Thurman in 'Pulp Fiction' or Clint Eastwood in 'The Good, the Bad and the Ugly' - all smokers - and all the more wonderful as characters because of that very fact.

Things have changed. The Marlboro Man is dead. The iconic cigarette ad actor died of lung cancer. Even James Bond, who in the original Ian Fleming books smoked 70 a day of a specially prepared Turkish and Balkan tobacco blend from 'Morlands of Grosvenor Street', has given up and is smoke free since the aptly named film, *Die Another Day* two decades ago.

Today, smoking has turned bad, not just killing its devotees, but helping wreck the environment and bringing forward the effects of climate change.

Globally, there are now more smokers than there have ever been, just over 1.1 billion. The biggest markets are in Asia, especially in China and India, and the continent consumes two-thirds of all tobacco grown on the planet.

In China, the nation that is both the largest producer, and also the largest consumer of tobacco in the world, some 2,043 cigarettes are smoked every year for each person in the country. In Russia that figure is even higher at 2,295, while in Canada it is 1,021, the USA is 1,016, Australia is 917, the UK is 827 and New Zealand is a far healthier 685.

The crushing impact of tobacco on human health is well documented, indeed the World Health Organization state that 'tobacco kills up to half its users'. What is not so well known is that tobacco also contributes 0.2% of all CO_2 emissions on the planet. If we add the fact that the single most common item of litter on the planet is the cigarette butt, the toxic chemical filled single-use plastic so commonly mistaken for food by wildlife, then we can understand the enormity of the problem. To top it off, many of the increasing number of large wildfires are started by stray cigarettes.

Incredibly, some smokers presently get their only fresh air of the day from going outside for a cigarette.

There are many ways to stop smoking, such as hypnosis, patches, drugs, gum, e-cigarettes, counselling, acupuncture, quit clubs, even quit apps. Many successful non-smokers would even suggest that friendly bribes, like being offered a vacation to give up, also work. As might embarking on a new relationship with a non-smoker, volunteering in a hospital, having children, taking up sports, or living on a desert island.

If you do smoke and want to 'un-addict' yourself from tobacco - the world, literally, will be thankful you did.

Impact: Remove up to 0.2% reduction in global carbon dioxide emissions.
Difficulty: Super hard.
Money-saving: Yes £1000+
Action: Just stop smoking. See smoking for what it is - smelly, deadly, and costly.

I Choose This Task ☐

Live in an Efficient Property

Not everyone lives where you expect. Tennessee-born singer, Tina Turner, lives in Switzerland, has done for over a quarter-of-a-century, and even has Swiss Nationality. Hollywood star John Travolta lives 2440 miles away from Tinseltown by road, but that doesn't matter, his fly-in house in Florida has its own runway where the trained pilot keeps his plane. Quintessential English actor Colin Firth has a home in Italy and Italian citizenship. In an incredible twist of politics, Boris Johnson, having been born in New York, could run for US President, while Donald Trump, by virtue of having a Scottish mother, could run to be the UK Prime Minister.

In the modern world, the USA is run by an Irish American whose Biden ancestors came from England - and were still living there in 1814 when the British burnt down the very building he now lives in - the White House.

Not everyone lives where you expect, some live, or can live, in places you would never imagine. The only certainty is that wherever we do live, we all have the option to choose, or at least change, what type of place we live in - be it good for our way of life - or bad.

The best way of feeling at home anywhere is to try and live in an efficient property that causes the occupants as little stress as possible, and in an area that is ideal to their needs. Get it right, and all is good, with people being more productive and happy. Get it wrong, and ending up in an inefficient home in the wrong area, and that can leave the occupant insecure, overcrowded, uncomfortable, and financially vulnerable. All factors along the path to depression, low-self-esteem, stress and anxiety.

Bought or rented, where people choose to live and how efficient their home is in terms of facilities also makes a big difference to the environment.

Living in an inefficient home costs the planet dearly. Location is a big factor. If your home is 50 miles from work and you commute there every day, that is around 20,000 miles a year in fuel costs and exhaust pollution, never mind other factors such as parking, car wear and tear, tolls, or wasted hours driving instead of working. If your home is energy inefficient, for example having gas, oil, or coal heating, instead of on-site solar or ground heat pump, or piped-in renewable energy from hydro, geothermal, solar or wind sources, then you are doing the planet no favours - and definitely wasting your own money in the process. A lack of insulation also makes a home massively inefficient, costing money and wasting energy. The home itself may be inefficient by being too big or too small for your needs. Most homes are also just plain inefficient, from an individual point of view and an environmental one, because they are filled with too much 'stuff', most of which is not properly stored for the rare occasions when it is needed. Then there are built-in inefficiencies to homes, such as overly big or small rooms, or badly designed and badly sited homes that, for example, don't catch the warmth of the sun or are built in flood areas.

Changing these factors to make the location, energy source, insulation, size, storage, and design more suitable to our individual needs, may seem hard but can be done bit by bit. Like most things in life it just needs an actual decision to be made - to live in a property that is good for our needs - and then commit to making the necessary changes to make it happen.

As home owners or renters, we can almost always change location - or we can change the homes we already live in to become more efficient for our real needs. Sometimes a clear out or a 'for sale' sign is all it takes to start.

Impact: Efficient homes reduce CO_2 emissions and improve wellbeing.
Difficulty: Easy, or very hard.
Money-saving: Yes £500+
Action: Is your home inefficient? If so, make a decision to change for the better.

I Do This Already  **I Choose This Task** ☐

Clear Your Medical Waste Safely

We all love a good bucket list - filled with all those great places and wonderful things we would like to do before we leave this planet with a smile on our face. Among the more popular items on a typical bucket list are: visit the Grand Canyon, go skydiving, see the northern lights, swim with dolphins, see the Pyramids, travel around Europe, take a cruise, ride an elephant, go zip-lining, get a tattoo, or run a marathon. Other, more common practical bucket list items include, get married, buy a house, save money, lose weight, get fit, have a child, donate blood, even write a book.

One sure thing also on many people's list is to attend one of the massive music festivals around the world, be it Coachella in California, Tomorrowland in Belgium, Sziget in Hungary, Ultra in Miami, Lollapalooza in Chicago, Brazil's Rock in Rio, Exit in Serbia, Roskilde in Denmark, Mawarzine in Morocco, Reading Festival in England, even Donauinselfest in Austria and Summerfest in Wisconsin, both of which claim to be the biggest in the world.

In the eyes of many though, the greatest of all open air music festivals on the planet is Glastonbury, in England, which has been running since 1970 and hosted almost every significant musician and band.

Now, here's the thing, many festivals are associated with drug taking, and in 2019 Glastonbury's organisers launched a 'don't pee on the land' campaign - and with good reason. Soon after the event, researchers found the level of drugs such as MDMA in the nearby River Whitelake from public urination were at levels dangerous enough to harm wildlife in the river - especially local eels. By pure coincidence that years line-up included noted natural historian David Attenborough - the narrator of the Planet Earth TV series, and bands The Killers, The Cure, The Vaccines, and The Chemical Brothers!

Drugs and medicines, the legal ones at least, have made a massive difference to our world and have certainly been one of the major contributing factors in helping human life expectancy on the planet go from 32 years in 1900 to today's 73 years. However, as so few of us know how to store medicines correctly (anyone still keeping them in the bathroom, normally the wettest room in the house, for example?), and with so many of us still keeping medicine cabinets full of old drugs, there are considerable potential dangers. The most obvious is that they may get into the wrong hands (like children or pets) or eventually be disposed in the wrong way - like down the toilet.

We wouldn't give our children or pets our old drugs directly, yet so many of us are quite happy to simply flush them down the toilet - where they can get back into the water system, our rivers and our seas - then back into us through the food chain.

Every country has different systems in place for drug and medicine disposal. In the USA, there are regular sponsored 'take back' programs in local areas, while many pharmacies, such as Walgreens, have special 'safe medication disposal kiosks' where unwanted, unused or expired medicines can be disposed.

In the United Kingdom, Canada, Australia, and New Zealand, almost all pharmacies will take back unwanted medicines, while that is mostly the same throughout the European Union. They all strongly dissuade people from flushing medicines down the toilet - mostly because not every sewerage plant can treat every chemical in waste water.

Most pharmacies advise to check your medicine cabinet every six months and to immediately return for disposal any medicines not being used.

Impact: Reduction in unwanted chemicals in landfills, water systems, and food chain.
Difficulty: Easy.
Money-saving: No.
Action: Check medicine cabinet and remove old tablets and medicines.

I Choose This Task

Buy the Product not the Problem Packaging

Do you remember the build up to the year 2012? There were a large number of media outlets happy to print a whole range of stories suggesting that, according to the Mayan calendar, the world would end on 21 December 2012. So engaging was the idea that a blockbuster $200m 'end of the world' Hollywood movie was made entitled '2012' starring John Cusack, Chiwetel Ejiofor, and Amanda Peet. Even Australian Prime Minister of the time, Julia Gillard, made a hoax speech where she confirmed the end of the world was coming and signed off with 'good luck to you all'. Strange days indeed.

In the end, as we all now know, nothing, nought, nada, zip, zilch, zero happened. We all got back to being 'not dead' and saying we never believed it anyway, even though actual sales of food, water, firearms and underground blast shelters had been booming in the countdown.

In many ways, we may have missed one real end of an era event that could have had an impact on the future of the planet that year. A well-known soda drink which, since 1915, had been making an iconic returnable and reusable 6.5 ounce bottle, finally stopped production in the United States on 9 October 2012. The last ever bottle was sold at auction for $2,000. All the soda brand's remaining bottled versions in the USA were then only recyclable.

Many other drink makers since the 1970s have also ended their bottle deposit schemes, suggesting consumers prefer bottle and can recycling. Sadly, as much of the world's litter and plastic pollution comes from drinks containers, this patently hasn't helped the planet.

Marketing Departments 1 - Earth 0

Perhaps it's time to just buy products - not the problem packaging.

It is important to note that packaging is important. Good packaging can keep foods fresh, medicines hygienic, stops liquids from leaking, and helps us transport items safely. The problem is not that we have packaging, but we are using the wrong type of packaging, or worse, the packaging is single-use, and more than likely (90.5% chance if it is plastic) never going to be recycled at all. Even worse, the packaging uses up massive amounts of energy and resources in its production. Even worse than the first even worse, the packaging may be entirely for show - not function or purpose - such as the packaging within packaging on luxury goods, toys and high-end foods.

In a perfect world we would have a circular system, where certain types of packaging, could be made using sustainable materials and renewable energy, and be durable enough to be re-used time and time again for their purpose, ending their days being recycled or composted, with a financial incentive to ensure each stage of the system works. However, until this happens, there are many things real people can still do.

The most obvious is to shop wisely and not buy the problem packaging in the first place. If we want bananas, a fruit already in its own natural (peel) container, just buy bananas, not a plastic bag filled with bananas - and transport them in your own bag or box. If you are going to buy a laptop, buy just a laptop, and leave the packaging box in the store.

If you can, try to buy zero plastic wrapped items, except obviously importantly packaged items, like medicines. If you can, use refill food stores in preference to supermarkets, and take your own containers.

Most of all, if something is overpackaged, or packaged in plastic when a more renewable packaging could be used - let the company making it know.

Impact: Could ensure removal of up to 90% of plastic packaging.
Difficulty: Easy - but restricts choice.
Money-saving: Yes £10+
Action: Choose to not buy products with unnecessary packaging.

I Do This Already ★ I Choose This Task ☐

Go Off-Peak to Save Money, Hassle, and the Environment

The highest point in Wales, at an elevation of 1085m (3560ft), is Mount Snowdon, one of the most beautiful natural locations on the planet. The mountain traditionally has six walking routes to the top, each for different levels of experience or fitness. Whichever you take, you will be sure to feel at one with nature and can put aside all stresses and strains of your daily life ... or that is supposedly the theory.

In reality, in the summer of 2021, the mountain was so busy at weekends it had periods when hikers were literally falling over each other and then had to endure hour-long supermarket style queues at the top waiting to physically reach the peak. There were even reports of scuffles breaking out.

Perhaps it may have made more sense if the stressed out hikers had climbed to the peak when it was off-peak! Such as midweek, very early morning, or in a different month. But most humans don't operate like that.

This situation is not unique, several popular hikes in National Parks around the world, such as Rocky Mountain National Park in Colorado, have felt compelled to introduce permit systems for visitors. Unbelievably, even Mount Everest, the highest mountain in the world, has busy period queues.

Going 'off-peak' to the peak may seem sensible, but it's not just a good idea when climbing mountains. Going off-peak whenever possible in hundreds of situations can give you a much better experience, be much cheaper, and has a host of benefits for the environment. So, whether you are catching a train or a flight, booking a hotel, going to a cinema or restaurant, making a long drive, or even getting married - doing so off-peak is a skill we could all learn.

One simple mantra to hold dear is 'DOPE or COPE!', which stands for '**D**elightful **O**ff **P**eak **E**xperience or **C**rowds **O**f **P**eople **E**verywhere'.

If you are going on vacation, try to stay away from peak times, like school or national holidays. Not only does it save money but also means there's less chance of overstretching the resources of the place being visited. There's also less chance of creating traffic jams or airport congestion, even overfilling parking spaces - and more chance of missing the crowds.

Energy is a great example where the use of off-peak can really work. Many energy companies offer certain times of the day when they provide lower 'off-peak' prices, such as between 10pm and 6am. Powering an electric car, or running washing machines during these times can save money and has the extra benefit of helping the energy supplier even out demand for energy over the day - thus saving valuable resources.

One area where the environment and individuals (or couple in this example) can benefit from the use of off-peak timing is weddings - which are reported to cost an average of $33,900 in the USA. An average of one-third of that cost being spent on the reception venue. Over 75% of weddings in the USA take place between May and October and over 60% of weddings take place on a Saturday. This gives a great opportunity to make savings for anyone happy to get married between Sunday to Friday from November to April. It also has the environment friendly benefit of ensuring the venue is more efficiently utilised.

Restaurants try to even out their resources by having 'early bird' prices while bars have 'happy hours'. Sports facilities have 'quiet time' memberships, and cinemas have 'saver' prices for unbusy periods. Whatever, the off-peak period is officially named, call it 'good' - for you and the environment.

Impact: Saves resources and energy across many sectors.
Difficulty: Easy.
Money-saving: Yes £500+
Action: Utilise off-peak periods for the benefit of you - and the environment.

I Choose This Task

Drop the Box!
Go One Year Without TV

Is there anyone on any planet who doesn't love watching TV? Whether your TV comes from terrestrial channels, satellite, cable, or via streamed services like Netflix, Britbox, and Prime, we just can't get enough. Whether you are into news, soap opera, drama, crime, comedy, documentaries, talk shows, sports, music, horror, history, or any of a thousand different genres, modern TV can literally keep you informed, entertained or educated 24 hours a day, 365 days a year. Scotsman John Logie Baird and American Philo Farnsworth would be amazed at how far their early TV inventions have progressed.

Most of us have shared conversations over the years with friends, family, colleagues, and social media, about how excited/amused/disgusted/happy/emotional/sad/relieved we are about what just happened in the latest episode of Downton Abbey, Breaking Bad, Friends, Oprah, The Gilmore Girls, Sex and the City, Coronation Street, Game of Thrones, Love Island, Mad Men, etc., all the way back to the days of I Love Lucy, MASH and Dallas.

All this wonderment in one small box, or more correctly these days, all this wonderment in a, mostly, not very small and not very box shaped TV. In fact, Samsung's 'The Wall' TVs now go up to 292 inches while the average size of a TV in the USA is 55in - up from 25in back in 2000.

Where would we be without our TVs and our shared experiences of the great things we can watch and experience right in our own living room?

TV is great, keeps us entertained and brings us together. But here's the thing - too much does exactly the opposite. Overuse literally keeps us from living an actual life, saps our ability to work, be productive or communicate.

Real world data suggests that those who earn above $75k a year, who could easily afford all TV options, spend considerably less time watching TV than those who earn below $25k. There is surely a subtle message here.

The challenge in this chapter is to do something most people will find impossible - go just ONE year without watching TV.

And why do this?

Well, as the average person in the USA watches close to four hours of TV per day, that time could be put to better use for the environment and the individual.

Four hours equates to 28 hours of TV a week. To put this in context, that amount of time is four-fifths the amount of time the average person in France is legally allowed to work each week.

Just think what you could do with an extra four hours every day - all yours. The average garden takes less than 30 minutes a day to tend, the average real homemade natural meal takes less than 30 minutes to make. The average fitness workout takes less than 30 minutes. Doing just these three would save you money, keep you healthy, help the planet, and you would still have another two-and-a-half hours a day to do other stuff that wasn't TV.

Naturally, before you go on your one year TV free regime - it might be worth one final splurge - a total binge-fest weekend of some of the best and most inspirational environment themed films and documentaries. These could include *Planet Earth* (a BBC documentary that will make you love your planet more than your sister!) or similarly, *The Blue Planet* or *David Attenborough - A Life on our Planet*. Also, *Cowspiracy*, *2040*, and *Before The Flood*. All topped off with excellent films including *Erin Brockovich*, *Wall-E*, *The Lorax*, *The Boy Who Harnessed The Wind*, *Interstellar*, *Dark Waters*, *The Day After Tomorrow*, *Avatar*, *Geostorm* and *Local Hero*.

Impact: Releases up to 28 hours a week for people to spend helping the environment or doing other constructive activities.
Difficulty: Super Hard.
Money-saving: Yes £500+
Action: Switch TV off and unsubscribe from TV services. Enjoy the free time.

I Choose This Task ☐

Garden Like an Off-Grid Fugitive and Show the World Your Butt!

Since March 1950 the US Federal Bureau of Investigation (FBI) has kept a continuous and ever changing list in place of it's Ten Most Wanted Fugitives - a list, in the description of its creator, FBI Director J Edgar Hoover, of the 'toughest guys' the bureau would like to capture.

At the time of writing a total of 526 fugitives, just 10 of them women, have found themselves on the list in its sixty-plus years of existence. Their faces splashed on Post Office walls, public notice boards, posted on the internet, and seen in the news and on television - along with the reward information, a minimum of $100,000 for 'information leading directly to their arrest'. Among their number have been well-known fugitives including serial killer Ted Bundy (caught), 9/11 attack mastermind Osama bin Laden (killed), and James Earl Ray, the assassin of Martin Luther King Jr (captured in the UK).

An impressive 491 of the 526, or 93.3%, of those placed on the list have been apprehended or located. One fugitive, Billie Austin Bryant, was captured within two hours. The title of 'longest on the list' was also it's least assuming criminal, Victor Manuel Gerena, a bank security guard who literally drove off with $7 million from his employers, and spent 32 years on the list before being removed from it in 2016 - presumed to be living in Cuba.

These fugitives are mentioned because, to stay free, they literally need to disappear, go off-grid, and have minimal contact, to avoid capture - and it is exactly that frame of mind people need when approaching how to tend their garden. Simply assume you have no utilities, like water and electric, and can't keep running to the shops every ten minutes to buy stuff.

The first thing any 'fugitive gardener' needs in their garden is water - and one easy way to achieve that without having to deal with the water company for fear of getting caught, is to put a covered water butt (rain barrel) by a garage or house gutter and use it as a quick supply of water for your plants.

The second thing our fugitive would do is to grow quick and easy fruit and vegetables, ensuring less time at a store. Fruit trees are for fugitives playing the long game, while simple vegetables, salads, and herbs can be grown within weeks and used as needed. One great way of ensuring pollination of your plants is to have a beehive - with the added bonus of regular honey.

If our fugitive kept a lawn at their hideout, you could guarantee they would not want to be going to any CCTV camera filled fuel station for mower fuel. They would most likely make their lawn smaller and more manageable, leaving a good area to grow naturally for pollinating insects - or more trees to hide behind. The remaining lawn would be trimmed by a manual mower (hard work) or by means of a solar powered electric mower, or better still, an autonomous solar mower that trims while you plan your next moves.

Naturally, our fugitive's hideout would not want to be dealing with green waste or trash collections for fear of being recognised, so everything that could be composted, lawn cuttings or waste food, even shredded paper and card, would be turned into nutritious compost.

This type of off-grid, automated, easy-pickings, compost the evidence, gardening approach is not just for criminals, it is for anyone who cares about the environment. However, you could pretend you're like Harrison Ford in the 1993 film classic, *The Fugitive* - living like a fugitive and on the run for a crime you didn't commit - not murder, but climate change!

Impact: Growing 20% of your own food means 20% less global food transport.
Difficulty: Easy.
Money-saving: £500+
Action: Buy seeds and plants. Then water and weed until ready to eat.

I Choose This Task

Fly the Flag

The total area of planet Earth is 510,067,420 km2, of which just 29% is land, with the remaining 71% being water.

If you broke down the surface area of the planet into 1000 equal sized pieces - each would be just over half a million square kilometres (510,067 km2) in size. Incredibly, only 20 of these 1000 pieces would be needed to accommodate the United States. Think about this, a country that takes up less than 2% of the planet is its most powerful superpower, its ideals and culture, good and bad, being spread to every corner of the world.

Similarly, Canada would fill 20 pieces of the 1000, while Australia would need 16, and the European Union 9.

The United Kingdom would need just one. In fact, it is so small, it would fit into half that single piece. Yep, a nation that not too long ago had the largest empire ever seen, and controlled one-quarter of the planet, did so from an island that can't even fit into a one-thousandth piece of the Earth.

And why do we mention this? One word ... Projection.

Some countries, some ideas, some people, are so strong they project bigger than reality. How else does a place like Britain, a small, insignificant, island on a rainy, cold and windswept part of the planet, manage to have had such a big influence that English is the world's universal language spoken by 1.14 billion people. This is 21 times more people than actually live in England.

Projection of an idea, first by a few, then by many, tends to grow because the idea is right for that time in history. Think anti-slavery, the United Nations, the Olympics, the Red Cross, Oxfam, even football, theatre and cinema - all once just a possibility - now a global norm.

The planet is important - that idea should be projected wherever possible.

Nothing to do directly with the environment, but everything to do with the power of ideas, if you have ever seen the 2010 film *Inception*, directed by Christopher Nolan and starring Leonardo DiCaprio, Tom Hardy, Joseph Gordon-Levitt, Elliot Page, Ken Watanabe, Michael Caine, Marion Cotillard and Cillian Murphy, you may be familiar with a quote in the film said by Tom Hardy. It goes, 'you mustn't be afraid to dream a little bigger darling' and this is so true. Regardless of how small and timid the world's leaders have been in their lukewarm pledges to reducing climate change at the COP climate change conferences, that doesn't mean the rest of us should follow suit, sit back and do nothing. We can, and should, dream bigger and promote and 'project' the idea that we can beat climate change and create the tech and practicalities to make that dream come true in every way we can.

The film *Inception* also had another quote, said by DiCaprio, which goes 'Once an idea has taken hold of the brain, it's almost impossible to eradicate', and if that applies to any one thing in our modern world today it is the idea that the planet is dying before our very eyes and we must get the world onboard to realistically change this direction.

We need to 'fly the flag' for the environment of this Earth, both metaphorically and literally. We all understand the power of working together towards a common goal - and one method of reinforcing that is to always publicise our aspirations.

An actual symbol, a flag, is also a very simple way of letting everyone know we are all in the same boat. An environment flag has been designed - indeed it is printed on the back cover of this book and a real one made from 100% sustainably sourced cotton is available to buy - or make yourself from unwanted clothes and materials.

Whichever of the 1000 pieces of the planet you live on, please fly it at every opportunity you get.

Impact: No direct impact but reinforces the common goal.
Difficulty: Easy.
Money-saving: No.
Action: Go to **EnvironmentFlag.com** - Buy the environment flag or make your own. Fly the environment flag.

I Choose This Task ☐

Hold Back on the Cement

The largest hydroelectric dam in the world is the Three Gorges Dam, which crosses the Yangtze River in China. The reservoir it created covers an area of 403 square miles (1,045 km2) to a depth of 574 feet (175m). It retains so much water that, when full, it slows down the rotation of the Earth by 0.06 microseconds. It also, ever so slightly, changes the shape of the planet and moves the Earth's poles by 2 centimetres. Damn! Dams are cool.

The most famous dam in the world, with around a million visitors a year, is the 726 feet (221m) high Hoover Dam that spans the Colorado River between Nevada and Arizona, 30 miles southeast of Las Vegas. Begun in 1931 and finished in 1936, the dam created a 247 square miles (640 km2) reservoir, known as Lake Mead, which is similar in size to Singapore.

There are close to 60,000 large dams on our planet - large meaning 50 feet (15.24m) or higher. Not only do they supply power and store valuable water, they also create jobs and open up lands for irrigation or living that were once prone to drought or desertification. Dams also save thousands of lives by smoothing the worst effects of river flooding.

The environment downer with dams is they can cause problems such as sediment loss down river, human displacement, ecosystem change, even cause conflict between nations over loss of water. The really big problem with dams, however, is they tend to be built using cement. In fact, so much concrete (think 110 million standard five-gallon household buckets) was used to create just the Hoover Dam alone. As an aside, that same concrete, poured in the 1930s won't technically have fully 'set' until around 2030.

And why is cement and concrete such an issue? Well, an incredible 8% of all climate changing carbon dioxide in our atmosphere comes from its use.

Cement solves so many problems in our 21st century world. Giant construction projects, homes, businesses, transportation systems, flood and sea defences, utilities, almost everything in construction is easier to create using cement. Many of our most iconic structures, whether the Sydney Opera House, Empire State Building, Pentagon, Burj Khalifa, CN Tower, Fallingwater, Millau Bridge, even the 2,000 year old Pantheon in Rome were all created using cement.

Between a half and two-thirds of carbon dioxide emissions from cement come as a byproduct from a chemical reaction known as calcination during the making of the cement itself. A process that at the same time also requires massive amounts of energy to get to the high-temperatures required to make it happen.

The world uses over 3.5 billion tonnes of cement every year and that figure is only increasing. That's half a tonne of cement for each and every human on the planet - every year. Cement is not bad, but the overuse of cement is not good and that needs to be reduced wherever possible.

Solutions are being created within the construction industry itself, such as using renewable energy, creating alternative cements, even capturing the carbon, or storing it back in the concrete. Architects and planners are also more open to building around, and with, existing buildings, changing them completely without the need for full demolition.

Real difference is going to come from individuals who reduce climate impact by choosing to use cement in only its most relevant setting - and use more Earth friendly materials, such as wood or reclaimed materials, wherever they can. Cement in a brick house is understandable, but who needs a concrete path or patio when alternatives like stone are available - and prettier?

Cement is vital - but use of less 'carbony' (it's just been made a word) alternatives are just as important.

Impact: Reducing cement by half would reduce world CO2 emissions by 4%.
Difficulty: Culturally and economically difficult.
Money-saving: Yes-No-Maybe.
Action: Make a conscious effort to not use cement where possible.

I Choose This Task

Bike More - Walk More - Drive Less

What transportation system costs less than 50p a day to use, is powered by excess fats, takes you straight to the middle of the city or out into the wilds of the countryside or wilderness, has zero parking fees, is almost silent, is ticketless, one of the quickest methods for short journeys, and is known to relieve stress and improve a person's physical and mental well-being?

Chances are you probably already know the answer, but just in case you think it's a stolen limo or a hover board, the actual answer is ... a bike.

OK, the 50p clue was a bit of a cheat, but that comes from the cost of a good bike over its 'everyday use' lifespan of around five years, purchase of a good helmet, bike locks, new chains, tyres, lights and bits, plus insurance. (But does not include the cost of the almost obligatory fluorescent lycra shorts!)

Dependent on where you live, cycling is an absolute dream or your worst nightmare. Some countries, such as Iran and North Korea have on/off regulations about female cyclists being allowed to ride, and some countries are, anecdotally, just downright scary for bike riding, like Malta or Botswana.

Some countries, most notably the Netherlands, literally live and love bikes, have a complete national and local network of cycle routes which, for much of the time never have you sharing space with that country's most famous driver, the superfast Max Verstappen, or any other car driver. Whether in a city or a village, the Netherlands caters wonderfully for cyclists - and the health and financial benefits of that 'bike life' are well documented. This includes research suggesting Dutch cyclists make 27% of all their trips by bike, the results of which are not only a reduction in vehicle pollution but health benefits that add half a year to the life expectancy of the people and a boost to the economy of 3% of Gross Domestic Product (GDP).

For hundreds of thousands of years, humans, lately in the form of homo sapiens, adapted their bodies to walking and running - useful stuff when hunting or moving from place to place. There was no other form of transport until around 5,000 years ago when nomadic tribes in central Asia became the world's first known horse riders. Even so, we still walked. However, in the space of just one century, we have got rid of much of that activity and are now 'sit down' movers, doing most of our big mileage in any of the 1.4 billion cars now on the world's roads, or on trains, planes, buses and boats.

The average person on planet Earth today walks just 2.48 miles per day (4km) which adds up to 906 miles per year (1458 km). Read into this what you like, but, at least one study has shown that women walk more than men - by 3 miles a year.

Now what has all this to do with the environment? Well, if we live in an area suitable for cycling we may be able to emulate the Netherlands and make up to a quarter of our journeys without using fossil fuels. For a similar reason, if we took up trying to walk at least five miles a day (or around 9500 steps a day if you use a tracker/pedometer) then that would eradicate many of the short journeys we might otherwise take by car. Whether cycling or walking, both have proven health benefits and both activities will save an individual a considerable amount of money in having to buy fuel for journeys that didn't need to be taken by a vehicle in the first place.

One final bonus to taking daily walks or bike rides is the social aspect. Cycle groups are everywhere, as are walking groups - and it is so easy to get to know people and places you walk past every day than it ever could be zooming by at 60mph.

Impact: Reduction in fuel emissions by up to 27%.
Difficulty: It's as easy as riding a bike or taking a stroll.
Money-saving: Yes £500+
Action: Get bike, ride bike. Get shoes, walk in shoes. Forget you have a car!

I Do This Already  **I Choose This Task** ☐

Review With Green Glasses

Who doesn't love reading a good, or even a bad, review? Whether it's a film, book, concert, restaurant, product, location, service or hotel, they can be wonderful to read and can give a sense of whether the thing being reviewed is something we want for ourselves. Some make us laugh, some make us cry, some make us angry, but ultimately, we are in some way informed, and we can't get enough of them. Even school reports or personal work reviews.

Searching through the varying lists of the world's greatest ever movies, the classic 1939 film, *The Wizard of Oz* (yes, it is really that old) is almost always in every top ten. Of course, respected film reviewer Otis Ferguson at *The New Republic* magazine didn't know that fact at the time of its release, stating, 'it weighs like a pound of fruitcake soaking wet'. Acid words indeed, added to by Russell Maloney at *The New Yorker* who claimed it had, 'no trace of imagination' and was a 'stinkeroo'. How wrong can you be?

Lovers of the Harry Potter series of books know reviews can be very wrong indeed. How else would at least a dozen publishers review the manuscript sent into them by the author, JK Rowling, and turn the book down flat, not realising it would ultimately result in half a billion book sales, a major film series, and end up making the author so much money she could spend a million dollars every week of her life and still have over a $1 billion on her 100th birthday - now that's magic! She's not alone. Before finding fame, The Beatles were turned down by the Decca record label with the withering line 'guitar groups are on their way out'. Even NOMA, the uber-popular three starred Michelin Guide restaurant in Copenhagen, and at the time of writing, the 'Best Restaurant in the World' has enough 'terrible' reviews on TripAdvisor to put anyone off visiting (if you could get a reservation to cancel, of course).

Reviews should be factual - but the reality is that the majority are purely subjective, spurred as yay or nay by millions of personal and external factors. A reviewer can use definitive facts about say, a new sports car, such as the 0-60mph speed, number of seats, price, size of car, etc., but they can only ever tell the reader/viewer/listener how they 'feel' when driving the thing - and that feeling will be different in every subsequent person who then sits in that same car and shares their own personal perspective.

With regard to the environment, the use of reviews is paramount to helping people see exactly what items, organisations, places and services are beneficial to the planet and which are increasing the problem of climate change or environmental destruction. The 'greening up' of reviews adds an extra dimension, previously ignored, to whether a thing is good or bad.

Many people already write reviews for things they purchase, locations they visit, organisations they deal with, and a million other things. It is incredibly useful when reviewing any product or service, they add at least one extra, purely factual, paragraph to the review. A small piece about the impact to the environment of the thing, place, service, etc. So, if a product has way too much packaging, or packaging made from non-recyclable materials, then let other possible future buyers of that product around the world know. If there are sustainable alternatives then state what they could be. All this information will be of great benefit to other buyers and, just as importantly, the makers of the product - many of whom have a bigger interest in reviews than their consumers and can improve from the feedback. If a thing is good for the environment then, similarly, let everyone know.

Reviewers - If you mean what you say - green what you say!

Impact: Important in encouraging product and service sustainability.
Difficulty: Easy.
Money-saving: Yes (for others).
Action: Review - and never forget to add a sentence or two on the environmental impacts of the product or service.

I Do This Already ★ **I Choose This Task** ☐

Dying to Help
Make the Last Thing You do on this Planet be a Good Thing

There are some incredibly wonderful people who have spent time on this planet over the years. People who brought joy and thought and fun to almost everyone they met, and left the Earth a much better place for their involvement in its history. One such person was an Indian born Englishman with an Irish passport who went by the name of Spike Milligan (1918-2002). He was best known as a comedian but was also a writer, poet, soldier, and environmentalist. Indeed, in 1971, in a period when concern for the planet seemed a minor thought to many in society he was reported to have smashed a window at the Hayward Gallery in London to protest his outrage that there was an 'art' installation that involved the killing of live animals.

The reason Spike Milligan is given mention here is simple, when he died, his final action was to leave a gravestone that still had everyone laughing. It had written, in Irish, the line *'Dúirt mé leat go raibh mé breoite'* which, when translated, reads literally as 'I told you I was unwell'.

Spike Milligan is not alone in leaving us with a smile on our faces or a thought in our mind. Mel Blanc, the voice of Bugs Bunny had, 'That's All Folks' as his gravestone epitaph, there's even a gravestone in Washington DC that simply states 'We finally found a place to park in Georgetown'. More poignant are Dr Martin Luther King Jr's, 'Free At Last' epitaph and Frank Sinatra's, 'The Best Is Yet To Come' - let's hope so.

Our final moments and the means in which we exit the planet are important for those we leave behind. Don't make your last action on this planet be something that ultimately helps destroy it.

The number of people who die on Earth each day is big - around 160,000 - a figure equivalent to twice the number of people that could be seated in the French National stadium in Paris, the Stade de France - or the equivalent of losing more people than live in the city of Dayton, Ohio.

When these people die, the way they say goodbye to the planet can have a massive impact on the environment. Dead people are no longer treated in the way they once were. We rarely bury people in a simple ceremony, at a natural site, within a short period, and a short distance, from where they died. Since the 1880s we've gone cadaver crazy, draining the blood from the bodies of our loved ones and filling it with a variety of solvents including methanol, ethanol and formaldehyde (even arsenic back in the early days). We then spend money on making up, dressing and jewelerising the body so it can be seen in an open casket. The body may be stored for weeks, then transported great distances, before finally being cremated or buried.

The cremation of a single body takes as much heat as is needed to warm a typical home in winter for a week, while the permanent resting place of the ashes or body takes up prime land filled with far transported headstones.

There is nothing wrong with marking the passing of people we love in these ways, but there is a shift in attitudes towards making funerals more green and natural. The so-called 'natural funeral' industry is taking funerals back to their simpler origins, but with the aid of hi-tech. Caskets are replaced with wicker baskets, or simple linen cloth, cremations are replaced with 'water cremations' (aquamation), while cemetery burials are replaced with woodland burials - trees planted in eternal forests with small QR coded markers.

If you are planning to leave us, make your last act a good one for the planet.

Impact: Up to 60m trees a year could be planted instead of headstones.
Difficulty: Easy.
Money-saving: Yes £1000+
Action: Instruct family and lawyers of your wishes for a natural funeral.

I Choose This Task

Tax Yourself! Create Your Own Personal Eco Tax

The brilliant author Mark Twain once pointed out that the difference between a taxidermist and a tax collector was that the 'taxidermist only takes the skin'. American columnist Bill Vaughan noted that 'tax collectors must love poor people, they create so many of them'. Even Albert Einstein, probably one of history's greatest-ever minds, is quoted as saying, 'the hardest thing in the world to understand is the income tax'. In complete contrast to these, Albert Bushnell Hart, the historian and author, took a far more optimistic view of taxation, suggesting that 'taxation is the price which civilised communities pay for the opportunity of remaining civilised'.

The most controversial quote about tax probably came from the billionaire one-time owner of the Empire State Building, Leona Helmsley, whose nickname was the 'Queen of Mean'. Infamous for serving an eviction notice on her only son's wife, Mimi Panzirer, the mother of her four grandchildren, soon after her son died of a heart attack, Helmsley eventually ended up in court in 1988 on tax-evasion charges. During the case she was quoted as saying 'we don't pay taxes, only little people pay taxes' - a line that became instantly famous as exemplifying the difference between the haves and the have nots in this world. She was found guilty and sentenced to four years in prison (she served 21 months). When Helmsley died at the age of 87 in 2007, she became even more famous, this time for leaving $12 million to her dog - a Maltese called 'Trouble'.

Few people enjoy paying taxes, while a rare few are creating their own personal tax by putting a percentage aside to help the environment.

The idea of creating an 'eco self-tax' is so alien to most people that it might be easier to translate the Voynich Manuscript (google that ... weird) or answer why men have nipples. It might even be easier to explain the rules and guidelines that govern tax decisions made by the USA's IRS, UK or New Zealand's Inland Revenue, Australia's ATO, Canada's CRA, or South Africa's SARS tax collection services.

For clarity, here's the basic premise. Chances are that if you make a lot of environment conscious choices, the main one being not to be a marketing department owned 'buy everything' crazed consumer, you'll probably end up spending a lot less money. In many ways, a similar thing happened during the first coronavirus lockdowns where a significant percentage who didn't have their normal daily fix of consumerism ended up with lots of extra money in their pocket. The UK, as an example saw an increase in extra savings of £190 billion - or £2,794 per person, while in the USA that figure was $1.5 trillion or $4,559 per person.

If you have surplus money created by not spending, or if you receive a salary raise but don't desire to change your personal budget upwards just because you can, then you need a plan. For many the simple answer is to invest in ethical or transformative 'eco' things you know about or believe in - such as wind power, sustainable forestry, environment tech, etc.

To eco self-tax or become an eco-altruist, is to take a small percentage of your spare money, say 10%, and put it into things that help the environment but don't, or most likely won't, give a direct return - such as environment charities, local community projects, education sponsorships, even seed investing in environmental start-ups or seed buying for community gardens.

Impact: The world gets extra investment in environment improving eco companies and projects.
Difficulty: Easy if you have the extra income or increased savings.
Money-saving: Yes-No-Maybe.
Action: Use any increase in salary or savings to improve planet not upgrade lifestyle.

I Do This Already  **I Choose This Task** ☐

Take Longer Holidays

We truly live on a very beautiful and diverse planet - with millions of different things to see and experience. The Grand Canyon, Machu Picchu, Venice, Uluru, Mount Fuji, Wulingyuan, the Serengeti, Times Square, the Great Wall of China, the Pyramids, the Burj Khalifa, the Rock of Gibraltar, the Amazon River - there are so many places that give an understanding of how awesome, in the truest sense of the word, our world can be.

We are also fortunate in the fact that most of the world is accessible in a way our ancestors would have thought impossible. We can literally visit five continents in just one day using scheduled airlines, a feat first completed by Norwegian, Gunnar Garfors, and Brit, Adrian Butterworth on 8 June 2012. They started in Istanbul (Asia) at 1.10am, flew to Casablanca (Africa), then Paris (Europe), on to the Dominican Republic (North America), before flying to Caracas, Venezuela (South America), getting there two hours before midnight.

The more we travel the more we learn and can appreciate the natural beauty of our planet, its wildlife and incredible plants, and our own different human cultures. Travel allows us to stand next to a giant Redwood tree, find ourselves unable to buy chewing gum at Disneyland, accept the Ethiopian year is seven years behind our 'normal' year, realise jet lag feels worse travelling from west to east, watch 150 tonne blue whales off the coast of Sri Lanka, enjoy a traditional Christmas picnic in Argentina, experience the free light show that is the Northern lights (Aurora borealis) and know there is another version at the south pole called Aurora Australis, stand on the Eiffel Tower knowing it can change shape by up to 15cm dependent on the weather, or watch the shortest scheduled flight on the planet (59 seconds) between two Scottish islands - Westray and Papa Westray.

Vacations are great. They expand the mind, relieve stress, put smiles on our faces, and introduce us to new people. The downer is they also wreck the environment through the massive amounts of carbon dioxide spewing from planes, cars and boats carrying us from location to location.

Therefore, with a smile behind the seriousness of what is being suggested here, we note that this particular task - number 93 - is possibly the most difficult of all the 100 tasks in this book.

Task 93 is quite simply to stop taking short holidays and instead double, triple, or even quadruple their length.

Yes, you heard correctly, if you are going to help the planet, take longer trips wherever possible. If you are going somewhere - go do it properly - see as much as you can - enjoy the culture - and do it in a less hassled manner. Why take four one week long overseas holidays a year, when you could take one month really getting to know a place? In an instant, you have reduced your flying time, and the CO2 it creates, to a half, or even a quarter, of what it would have been. But even more can be done.

Take a look at how many non-vacation flights you do each year on average and try to halve that number. Change 'fly to' meetings to online meetings wherever possible - especially the boring ones! Don't take any short flights when you could get a train instead. Best of all, if you do have to go somewhere for business - make the bit before or after your trip a holiday or working holiday. Flying from London to Australia for a conference? If you can, smarten your time - fly in small steps, stopping along the way to meet other clients or colleagues - and stay in each country for an extended period.

Need to travel? Make it efficient and money wise and link it with other things.

Impact: Halving flights could save up to 1.2% of all global CO2 emissions.
Difficulty: Easy, and fun.
Money-saving: Yes £500+
Action: Make fewer, but longer trips and reduce your flights.

I Do This Already ★ **I Choose This Task** ☐

Vote

One of the greatest and, according to those who were there, most realistic war movies ever, was Steven Spielberg's 1998 film, *Saving Private Ryan* starring Tom Hanks and Matt Damon. The film told the story of the D-Day Normandy landings in June 1944, and the first fifteen minutes are enough to persuade anyone about the true horrors of warfare.

The film, though set in France, only used one real location in that country for filming, the 172 acres set aside as the American Cemetery the day after the battle, at Colleville-sur-Mere. The last resting place of 9,386 mostly twenty-something young men who died fighting on the Normandy Beaches so that democracy could live and thrive in the future. There are very few visitors to the cemetery, no matter how tough, that don't at some point shed a tear.

Young Allied soldiers, whether in Normandy, Dunkirk, Tobruk, Iwo Jima or other parts of the world were not alone in fighting and dying for freedom. In a place called Kohima on the India/Burma border, a memorial for the British, Indian, and Gurkha units who fought and died, holding back the mighty Japanese army reads:

When you go home, Tell them of us and say,
For your tomorrow, We gave our today.

Stirring words about normal people who died in the knowledge their ultimate sacrifice was a price worth paying - freedom and democracy for their families, friends and nation.

It was important then, and should always remain important, that all men and women of the world should never again have to fight or struggle to simply have their voice or opinions heard.

In short, the journey for democracy and the ability to have our say was long and hard. Let's never waste the sacrifice of those who gifted us our freedoms and honour them by voting in every election - come rain, hail or shine.

This may sound simple, but if the environment is important to you then, when it comes to election time (local, regional, national), give your vote to the candidates who also see the environment as importantly as you do.

Don't stress too much about party lines - it is normally an individual you are voting to represent you - so make sure they at least share many of your views, hopes, and beliefs. If you are unsure of any candidates, and what they stand for, write or ask them directly what their environment policies are. If they don't reply or their reply is all waffle, then that is exactly what you will get from them after the election should they win.

Elections are not some non-event. If done correctly, they are the peaceful alternative to having to fight on the streets to decide what happens to your life and your village, town, region, or nation. Elections are not about, 'might is right' and allowing those with the biggest gang, or latest weapons, to take control - elections are about consulting every adult, whatever their gender or colour or position in life, and deciding who can best represent them.

Switzerland only gave the vote to women in 1971. Up to that time females could not truly decide what happened to their country or their environment. Amazingly, half a century later that struggle for representation seems to be forgotten with only 45% of those eligible to vote doing so. In the USA, a country where colour was once a bar against voting, the last Presidential election saw one in every three eligible voters decide not to vote. Similar numbers of absent voters are seen in the UK, Canada and New Zealand - but not Australia where it is seen as so important to have your say that you can be fined if you don't vote.

Many gave their lives so you could vote. Try not to disrespect their sacrifice. If you want change ... vote for it!

Impact: Possibly the greatest impact you can make to climate change.
Difficulty: Normally easy and free.
Money-saving: No.
Action: Choose a candidate who best meets your standards and ideals and cares about the environment as much as you do.

I Choose This Task ☐

Eat Together

American actor and director, Orson Welles (1915-1985), was one of the most talented and creative filmmakers Hollywood has ever produced, leaving us with two of the most outstanding entertainment moments in history - the 1938 radio adaptation of H.G. Wells, *War of the Worlds*, and the classic 1941 film, *Citizen Kane*. He also left us with one of the most relevant quotes ever voiced, and one that should be passed on to every generation: *'I prefer people who rock the boat to people who jump out'*. Great advice.

Another quote credited to Orson Welles is: *'If there hadn't been women we'd still be squatting in a cave eating raw meat ... we made civilisation in order to impress our girlfriends'*. This notion that civilisation and social interactions are better formed over food is not new, but does have some research to back up the idea that: *'The family that eats together, stays together'*; and *'Food tastes better when you eat it with your family'*.

Research at Oxford University in 2017 found that people who eat socially have a better feeling about themselves. Even so, the same research found that people still eat almost half of all their meals in isolation. The solitary diner, it appears, is a real thing, even for people who live in the same house.

If you are looking for families who eat together, we need go no further than those found on TV. The Waltons always ate together, as did the Brady Bunch, the Arnolds in The Wonder Years, the Cunninghams plus Fonzie in Happy Days, The Sopranos, the Banks family in the Fresh Prince of Bel-Air, and the Addams family ate together (although it was rumoured they ate one of their children). Even the Simpsons - Homer, Marge, Bart, Lisa, and Maggie eat together, and though they have too much pizza, they do their best, the kids get lots of exercise, and at least one child eats mostly fruit and vegetables.

Sitting down together to eat. Buying for two, three, four, or more, is always cheaper per head than buying for one - and normally much less wasteful.

Some 40% of Earth's land is used for food production, so, for those who care about the planet, reducing food waste by even a mere 1% through eating together is reason alone to start or maintain the tradition. Eating together at home also tends to mean more normal sized portions than if a person ate out, bought takeaway, or ate alone - saving even more forest and wilderness from being destroyed to become farmland - and instead doing its vitally important job of taking in carbon and giving out oxygen.

The social, financial, educational and health benefits of sitting around a table to eat, even just four or five times a week, have been proven time after time to be massively beneficial. Eating together, unless you live in a very, very, unhappy home, is a great stress reliever, has been shown to reduce the levels of substance abuse in families, help creativity, bridge generational, cultural and social differences, improve family or housemate bonding, improve communication - even improve academic results. It also saves direct energy as ovens, microwaves, toasters, steamers, kettles, dishwashers, etc., are used once, not two, three, four, or more times for individual meals.

Eating together tends to mean those involved have far healthier food, eat at regular times - and by helping in the prep, cooking, table laying, clearing, or dishwashing, etc., help to instil a good work and co-operative ethos.

Even for the most penny-pinching, self-obsessed person on the planet it is easy to see how eating together at home saves money, time and effort - and has the planetary bonus of saving energy and farmland. Those involved also get the very tasty benefit of sharing way more varied meals. Enjoy!

Impact: Possible 1% plus reduction of land needed for crops.
Difficulty: Moderately easy.
Money-saving: Yes £500+
Action: Set food times and share meals and mealtime chores.

I Do This Already ★ **I Choose This Task** ☐

Gold is Not Always Golden and Diamonds May Not be a Girl's Best Friend

Would you consider the idea of dumping gold and diamonds as personal jewellery?

Gold is ... well ... gold. It doesn't corrode, rust, or decay and is resistant to solar radiation and most acids. It is dense, easily workable, conducts electricity, can be stretched, melts easily, and it's shiny. Gold is accepted as the thing you get if you are the best, hence the gold medal in the Olympics, or talk of a 'gold standard' if something is in the highest bracket. All the known gold in the world, all 197,576 tonnes of it, could fit in just the ground floor alone of the 102-storey Empire State Building, meaning it is rare enough to be valuable, but common enough that we can all have a very small share.

Gold is universally accepted as being luxurious. It has been the final covering of ancient Pharaohs, worn by the wealthy and the famous for thousands of years, displayed as the sign of power in the crowns, rings and sceptres of Kings, Queens, Popes, tribal elders, and clan leaders. Even NASA use gold on their space craft and astronaut helmets, which is appropriate as almost all gold on planet Earth is thought to have come here from outer space, arriving in asteroid impacts over the past 4 billion years.

Diamonds, those lovely shiny pieces of carbon in solid form, whose name comes from the Greek word 'adamas', meaning 'unbreakable' are the hardest naturally occurring material in the world (alongside wurtzite and lonsdaleite if you can find them). The real strength of diamonds, however, is in their global image - they really are seen as, 'a girl's best friend' and are the de facto symbol of engagement. In the USA alone some 86% of all new engagement rings included a colourless diamond as the centre stone.

One simple way of helping the environment is to back off from gold wherever possible. If you have any gold, you might consider selling it and using the money on something that isn't quite as bizarre as buying a metal that originates in outer space, requires the destruction/movement of 4 plus tonnes of land for every ounce found, contaminates rivers, involves the use of mercury, cyanide and other chemicals in its mining, displaces people, and is documented to involve child labour - all so it can, mostly, end up hidden away underground again. This time in a vault or safe.

Diamonds, similarly, have a massive environmental impact. Indeed, it is estimated that for every single carat of diamond an incredible 250 tonnes of earth needs to be moved. A particularly nasty aspect in the underworld of that industry are 'Blood Diamonds', which involve civil wars, warlords, murder, modern-day slavery, bribery, and smuggling.

If you need jewellery for something genuinely culturally important to you - like a wedding ring - then something that truly exemplifies the wedding motto of 'something old, something new' may be to buy a used wedding ring or a hand me down from beloved parents, grandparents and family who came before - and have it reworked by craftspeople to fit your modern taste. Engagement rings, if actually needed, could also be, literally, 'second-hand' (pun intended), or upcycled. Considering the average US couple spent £2765 ($3756) on a new ring, while their UK equivalent spent £1900 ($2581), this could also mean quite a financial saving.

One nice return to older ways is the move to wooden rings. In many ways this is replacing one form of hard to get carbon capture (diamond) with a much easier to obtain form of carbon capture (wood).

Impact: Reduces destruction of land and pollution of waterways.
Difficulty: Easy.
Money-saving: Yes £500+
Action: Rework old gold and diamonds into modern jewellery or use other materials.

I Do This Already  **I Choose This Task** ☐

Ask Where and How Your Stuff is Made or Grown

If you have ever wondered what Africa and Antarctica share in common (hasn't everyone?) then here's something to add to your list - not only are they the two continents most affected by climate change but, at the time of writing, these are the only two continents on the planet that do not have a company that directly supplies parts for the Apple iPhone. From China to Australia to Brazil to Mexico to the UK, and including a rainbow of 24 other nations in-between, the iPhone is made from parts manufactured or assembled on every other continent.

The iPhone is not alone in having a United Nations of suppliers, most things these days are made using the best (or sometimes cheapest or most cost effective) suppliers - wherever they may be in the world. Most cars are made using parts from all over the planet - even the iconic Mini car, a symbol of everything British, now German owned, had a pre-Brexit story about how its crankshaft would have crossed the English Channel four times if it was sold in mainland Europe, simply down to complex supply chains.

Similarly, many of our foods travel thousands of miles from where they are grown to factories in other countries. They are turned from ingredients into food products. Then travel thousands more miles to distribution centres in other countries. Then even more miles to supermarkets - to then be driven to our homes. Finally, the food product, once home, and having finished an epic journey longer than that made by Marco Polo, has, according to the United States Food & Drug Administration (FDA), only a two-thirds chance of being eaten.

We live in a very complex and finely tuned world of mass production, monoculture food production, and 'just in time' distribution, which worked great for many consumers and businesses (but not always for the environment) until along came the Covid Pandemic and all of a sudden moving stuff around the world with ease became very difficult and increasingly expensive. All of a sudden people and governments realised their vulnerability to reliance on anything from far off places.

Today, wherever we live, the trend appears to be leaning more towards locally produced goods, especially for food items, while those from overseas need to be more specialised (like silicon chips) or completely unique to other areas of the world (like Champagne). A further trend is towards sustainable and ethically sourced foods (like 'shade grown' and 'fair trade' coffee).

If possible, go local for your foods (or better still, grow your own). Take a look at where you live and see if you can get most of the food and items you need from within a few miles or so of where you live. Farmers' markets are useful sources of locally produced items, but even global supermarkets are now making space and highlighting locally produced goods in their stores.

Learn where the things you fill your life with everyday - 'your stuff' - is actually coming from. Did that chicken you eat come from a cooped up colony cage, from an enclosed barn, or was it completely free-range? Is that cornflake made from a genetically modified crop? Did that shaving cream travel 10,000 miles to get to your bathroom? Is that shirt or trainer made using prison labour, modern day slavery, or child workers?

Do an inventory and research everything you buy or want to buy before deciding to stay, or become, a future consumer of that product.

Impact: Massive reduction in transportation mileage of goods.
Difficulty: Easier to say than do.
Money-saving: Yes.
Action: Research the journey and impact of everything you use or eat.

I Choose This Task

Have a Good De-Clutter

Our planet is totally unique and the only place in the known universe that has life. It is in just the right place to be served by the Sun it orbits, the so-called 'Goldilocks Zone', being 'not too hot and not too cold'. It has a strong, protective, atmosphere, an abundance of water, and enough oxygen for life. It feeds us and is rich in elements that can be reworked to form pretty much anything we want to create - from houses to bridges to cars, even to banana slicers or golf balls. It is perfect - a genuine Eden by any definition.

Astronomers have long studied the universe beyond our solar system for signs of any other planets out there - the so-called 'exoplanets'. According to the European Space Agency there are 100 thousand million other stars in just our Milky Way alone (and this is just one of billions of other galaxies). Theoretically, Earth could have an exact twin - but we ain't found it yet!

The first exoplanet like anything in our Solar System was discovered in 1999, in the Pegasus Constellation. It was officially called the slightly boring HD 209458b, but is better known as Osiris, after the Ancient Egyptian god. Since then some 4,905 exoplanets have been discovered, with 60 of them believed to be 'potentially habitable'. As even the most Earth-like planet, Kepler-452b, is 1,400 light years away, it is highly unlikely we will stand on an Earth 2.0 before we destroy the Earth 1.0 we already have.

So, here we are, on a planet that has only a finite amount of resources. It would be wonderful if the world could continue making billions of products and things knowing that, at any time, we could simply re-purpose or recycle everything when it was no longer needed to make new things. Sadly, not even 12% of plastics we have already made have been recycled.

We need to slow down our consumption! We need to de-clutter our lives!

The joy of de-cluttering is wonderful. Most of us have spent all our lives over-consuming 'stuff', and spending a fortune doing so without too much benefit. Look around your home - there is a good chance you will have mountains of things you literally never use, never need, and never want.

A cluttered home can lead to a cluttered mind. It is also worth noting that, as 60% of all falls occur in the home, your clutter might get you clattered. It is time to be free of these things.

There are many methods of de-cluttering, but the simplest is to imagine how your want your ideal home to be - then think of everything in your home as trash until it has been given a designation that fits in with that goal. You then split everything into four piles in strict order - *Need, Give, Sell, Recycle*.

Need is the hardest category, but one handy way of working out the *Need* pile is to ask yourself if you have used that thing in the last 12 months. If not, it is moved down to the *Give* category which is where you think of a charity or everyone you know, then work out if any of them need that breadmaker you have never used. If not, then it's *Sell* time - and we all love cash. Finally, if the item can't be re-purposed, it is put in the *Recycle* pile. When you've done, put the *Need* pile in their own special, accessible, and memorable places.

Money will be made, money will be saved, charities will be grateful, friends will smile at your well thought out gifts, space will be gained, our homes will look better, things will be easier to find, cleaning will be simpler, you may even find really useful things you never knew you owned, but the biggest winner from de-cluttering is the environment. This comes mainly from being able to visualise the unnecessary trash we have brought into our homes over the years and just how wasteful it all is - and brings to focus how quickly we have been using up our only planet's valuable resources.

Impact: Anything that removes over-consumption saves finite resources.
Difficulty: Easy and fun.
Money-saving: Yes £100+
Action: Check your 'stuff' with *Need*, *Give*, *Sell,* or *Recycle* in mind.

I Choose This Task

Measure Your Carbon Footprint

There have been a handful of great Presidents in the history of the United States - George Washington, Abraham Lincoln, Franklin D Roosevelt, John F Kennedy, Ronald Reagan, etc. BUT, how do they compare to the truly brilliant fictional Presidents that Hollywood has thrown our way over the years.

It seems the US has had far better unreal Presidents since the beginning of cinematography than it ever had real ones. Who could be a more American hero than President James Marshall, played by Harrison Ford, in *Air Force One*? Who could have more common sense than President Dave Kovic, played by Kevin Kline, in *Dave*? Who could be smarter than President Jed Bartlet, played by Martin Sheen, in *The West Wing*? Who could be cooler under crisis than President Thomas J Whitmore, played by Bill Pullman, in *Independence Day*? Who could ever be more steel willed than President Thomas Wilson, played by Danny Glover, in *2012*? Who could have been tougher than President James Sawyer, played by Jamie Foxx in *White House Down*? Who could have guided the country better than President Mackenzie Allen, played by Geena Davis, in *Commander in Chief*? And finally, who could have been more honest to his word than President Andrew Shepherd, played by Michael Douglas, in *The American President*.

Yes, there were some absolute howlers as well, Presidents who were that bad they could actually have been real, such as the cool but bad negotiator President James Dale, played by Jack Nicholson, in *Mars Attacks* or the very bizarre President Merkin Muffley, played by Peter Sellers, in *Dr Strangelove*.

Whichever President you think of, real or unreal, it is hard to imagine any of them, except perhaps Pres Dave Kovic, would really know something that could literally save the world from actual destruction: their own carbon footprint.

It is said that a great way of starting to solve a problem is first recognising there is an actual problem. Then checking to see if you yourself are part of the problem or part of the solution.

With regard to the environment and climate change, the recognition there is an actual crisis is solid science. Yes, in our strange world there are still those few who can't, or don't want to, see the forest fires, the almost frequent 'one in a century' storms, the floods, the extinction of whole species of flora and fauna, the pollution of rivers and oceans, and the droughts and desertification of once green land. However, the reality is that if you are driving towards a cliff edge, can see the drop in the distance ahead and 999 people out of 1000 are screaming at you to stop, do you really want to listen to the one who is shouting, 'it's all good'?

With regard to seeing if you are part of the problem, one great way of doing this is to take a check on a carbon footprint calculator and then use that as the start point. Many governments and government departments, such as the EPA in the USA, Gov.uk site in the UK, Natural Resources Canada, the EPA Victoria in Australia, and Gen Less government campaign in New Zealand have straightforward online carbon footprint calculators. Similarly, many environment and wildlife organisations such as the World Wildlife Fund for Nature (WWF) also have carbon footprint calculators.

Interestingly, at least one of the big oil companies has a calculator which once completed offers users a means of paying money to offset your annual carbon footprint from using their fuel. If they were really climate conscious perhaps they could offer to match the amount being paid. Until then, if LOL is in the dictionary these days (it is), I'd like to use it here.

Impact: Understanding our part in the problem is 100% better than not.
Difficulty: Easy.
Money-saving: Yes-No-Maybe.
Action: Take a carbon footprint test from a trusted source.

I Do This Already  **I Choose This Task** ☐

Volunteer!
Your Country and Planet Need You

There is a story of a lady called Helene Podliasky who worked for the French Resistance during World War Two. She was captured in 1944 by the Nazi secret police, the Gestapo, and after being tortured, was sent to the Ravensbruck concentration camp north of Berlin. Starved, stripped bare, tortured, left to stand in ice and snow, Helene formed a bond with eight other female Resistance fighters when they were sent to work in a labour camp. Their prospects were bleak, but even as their life chances were fading through starvation and cruelty they did something that was truly beautiful. Each day they received a bowl of thin soup, and each day they all took one spoonful and put it in a 'bowl of solidarity'. That bowl was then given to the woman who needed it most at that moment. It was, quite literally, a life saver, and psychologically a symbol of hope.

It seems the basic nature of most people, even in times of great difficulty, is to want to help others - especially if there is a common goal. That strength and will to work together to make the best of any situation, to fight to the end, is something our planet could most certainly do with today.

Whether we realise it or not, whether we are optimistic, stoic, scared, blissfully ignorant, or pretend ignorant of the facts, there is a tipping point heading our way with regard to climate change. A point where it will be too late to make any difference at all. We, or more realistically our children, grandchildren, or descendants will see the end of most life on our planet.

Heavy stuff indeed, but science says it is also preventable. All we need to do, whoever we are, is play our small part in making change while we still can.

Most of us feel helpless when it comes to the environment. We see things like the COP climate change conferences and feel nothing but despair. The science is there but many leaders, governments, and corporations seem just content, or even pressured, to 'kick the can down the road'. There is always a reason for inactivity, half measures, all sweetened by nice sounding PR.

The thing is, it is that same 'most of us' who can make the biggest change of all. We can make personal changes, sure, but we can also re-pivot our careers, businesses or even our free time, to doing things that will help, not harm, the planet. If we want governments and companies to take the environment seriously, then we can let them know via the ballot box or where we spend our money, whether they are doing a good job.

Making a personal choice to be carbon neutral is a start - walking or cycling more, using public transport, growing a few plants, insulating your property, changing your home energy to renewable, saving for an electric car, buying only what you really need, using less single-use packaging, learning how to recycle properly, even planting a carbon-eating hedge. They all help.

If we are in a mighty battle for the environment then why not conscript yourself - volunteer now for things like cleanups in your own street, village or area. Work with neighbours and local groups to make sure your area is the best it can be, not just neat and tidy, but somewhere that has enough trees, good water, maybe a community garden, and certainly a place to share information on things like solar energy, heat pumps, upcycling, even healthy recipes.

Volunteering just 2% of your year would give a week for the environment - time to make a difference, meet people, be part of a community, learn new skills, be outdoors, gain confidence, see new places, and have fun.

Volunteer! Your country and planet need you more than ever.

Impact: Everyone volunteering 2% of their time is 1.3 trillion hours a year.
Difficulty: Easy, and very social.
Money-saving: Yes-No-Maybe.
Action: Devote time to volunteering. If a group doesn't already exist - set one up.

I Choose This Task

It's Decision Time!

You've Read The 100
Tasks That Can Help
The Environment

Now Pick
Which One Of
The 100
You Are Going To
Complete?

How Many Of The 100 Tasks Do You Already Do?

To help your decision, it is useful to know which of the 100 tasks you already do as part of your daily life.

Tick the number of each task you already do, and don't stress any about task 55, we've saved some ink and already ticked it for you. The average person normally does just **9** tasks already.

1 ☐	21 ☐	41 ☐	61 ☐	81 ☐
2 ☐	22 ☐	42 ☐	62 ☐	82 ☐
3 ☐	23 ☐	43 ☐	63 ☐	83 ☐
4 ☐	24 ☐	44 ☐	64 ☐	84 ☐
5 ☐	25 ☐	45 ☐	65 ☐	85 ☐
6 ☐	26 ☐	46 ☐	66 ☐	86 ☐
7 ☐	27 ☐	47 ☐	67 ☐	87 ☐
8 ☐	28 ☐	48 ☐	68 ☐	88 ☐
9 ☐	29 ☐	49 ☐	69 ☐	89 ☐
10 ☐	30 ☐	50 ☐	70 ☐	90 ☐
11 ☐	31 ☐	51 ☐	71 ☐	91 ☐
12 ☐	32 ☐	52 ☐	72 ☐	92 ☐
13 ☐	33 ☐	53 ☐	73 ☐	93 ☐
14 ☐	34 ☐	54 ☐	74 ☐	94 ☐
15 ☐	35 ☐	55 ☑	75 ☐	95 ☐
16 ☐	36 ☐	56 ☐	76 ☐	96 ☐
17 ☐	37 ☐	57 ☐	77 ☐	97 ☐
18 ☐	38 ☐	58 ☐	78 ☐	98 ☐
19 ☐	39 ☐	59 ☐	79 ☐	99 ☐
20 ☐	40 ☐	60 ☐	80 ☐	100 ☐

Once completed, send the task numbers you already do to **#IDoTheseAlready**

#IDoTheseAlready **I DO** ____ **TASKS ALREADY**

The Task I Choose To Complete Is ...

TASK NUMBER

write task number here

SIGNED

DATE

Once completed, let the world know which task you have chosen and aim to complete at **#ChosenToSaveThePlanet**

#ChosenToSaveThePlanet

You've Done It!
You've Read the 100 Tasks.

Hopefully, you have now found the task you are happy to complete.

After so many pages, there is a good chance you may feel connected to this book, its ideas and even the author. So I feel I should thank you for reading - properly introduce myself - and wish you all the best with your choice from the 100.

It probably makes sense to start with a confession. The author of this book, a one-time, but long-time, journalist at the Daily Mail, is not, by so many definitions, an environmentalist. I drive a diesel, live in a house with almost zero insulation and an open fire, keep the lights on in my home way too much, love bonfires, leave the taps on when cleaning my teeth, travel whenever I can - and crime of crimes - I was the guy who created the world's first ever car fuel comparison website, PetrolBusters - now long owned then quietly dropped by the UK's Automobile Association (AA).

In my defence, I do recycle properly and have never littered. In fact I started my career working for a few months for Keep Britain Tidy. The diesel car is running its natural lifecycle and will be replaced by an electric car (unless this book sells badly and then there will be no car at all!), the planning application to upgrade the house (and insulation) has been lodged with the local council, the open fire is mostly log burning and will be replaced in time by ground pump heating and solar, the lights are powered on a renewable energy tariff, the bonfire is almost always made from garden hedge cuttings and branches, I live in an area with an over-abundance of water, the travel is always carbon offset by planting trees or giving them as gifts, and - economic crime of crimes - I paid penance for my fuel comparison site moment by spending a fortune I never got back to create the world's first national recycling database - an also long-gone UK based website where you could tick your type of waste and it would let you know the nearest and most appropriate place it could be recycled.

Credentials established, I should also mention that, yes, I have hugged a tree. Admittedly one that I was trying to tie a hammock to with my daughter. I've even pranced and danced around one when visiting the 275 feet (83.8m) tall General Sherman, the world's largest tree, in California's Sequoia National Park in the midst of a snowy winter. The dancing was really me stomping my feet trying to keep warm while taking steps in the snow and ice around the base of this truly magnificent tree to get an accurate measurement of its circumference - a pretty impressive 103 feet (31.4m) if you are interested to know.

Why the confession? Well, to be as straightforward as possible, I don't want to have to care about the environment at all. I would much rather spend my time having fun, meeting friends, seeing nice places and staying in lovely hotels. I would be happier writing a book about history, or cinema, or even that great and totally original thriller idea I've always wanted to put together called *The Berlin Sleepers*. I could do up a boat, spend time with my family, open a chess shop and cafe called *Chess Store* in the city of Chester and cheekily pick up the phone each day saying a tongue-tied, 'Chester Chess Store'. I might even persuade Rand McNally that we should make driving places more interesting by creating a new Road Atlas of the USA but making every location an anagram of its actual name (ie. New York = Worn Key, Los Angeles = Glee Salons, Houston = Nu Shoot, Washington = Thin Wagons).

Just think of all the fun that could be had.

In comparison, thinking about the environment, and the damage we've done to the planet is literally the most depressing thing ever. Writing about it, though fun, being quite distressing.

The bottom line - humanity has messed up. We have created our own version of the Star Wars *Death Star*, but one that can only fire inwards - and most leaders and companies don't seem to want to do anything real to change things - just wing it and hope.

The moment of real fear, for me personally, was the first time I heard that a common conversation among many women these days was not about 'when' they would have children, or 'how many' children they would have, but rather 'should I have children at all and bring them into this mess?'. This was the moment I saw as the psychological signpost that the war for the environment was truly being lost. All we had to do now was watch the ship called Earth sink into the long gone icy waters of its own titanic making.

Can we really sit on our backsides, ignore the science, and ignore the changes in climate we can see happening around us?

Well. Yes. We can. And we do! We've been ignoring it forever. It's not because we don't care, it's partly because most of us don't know exactly 'how' to care. Add to this that we think it's too big a problem to solve on our own - or the idea that it won't happen this week - or because we're happy leaving the problem to others - and you can see why we are ignoring all the signs of our destruction.

But, here's the thing. There is no 'Magic Bob', a mythical saver of the environment. He doesn't exist. Nor does 'Magic Betty', or any other non-existent superheroes we blindly assume are behind the scenes groovily saving the environment.

We can't ignore it any longer. It is up to us to take the place where we think Magic Bob would have stood, and do the things we think Magic Betty would have done to save the planet.

There is a tipping point fast approaching where it will be too late to change anything - but that moment has not yet come and this planet has the resources and the brains to fight this problem - and win.

There is a quote from a Canadian philosopher called Marshall McLuhan that people should think about when considering if they can play a part in helping the environment or not. Now long gone (McLuhan died in 1980), he had the foresight to note that:

There are no passengers on Spaceship Earth.
We are all crew.

How fabulous a quote is that to remind us of our responsibility?

Everything else but winning the climate change war must come second at the moment. That other book will have to go on hold (unless the profits from it go to an environment charity/project). The Chester Chess Store and cafe will remain unopened (unless it becomes a place to buy sustainable or second hand chess sets). The ever so funny anagram map of the USA will remain 'un-anagrammed' (unless it can be created to make money to 're-green' places).

In short, unless people re-pivot their lives, even slightly, so our environment problems become the source for solutions rather than fear, then we will continue to lose our planet to the damage we seeded earlier, but now reap in its planet killing harvest.

Having said all of this, I 100% believe that cimate change can be held back and the environment saved. But only if we start to see the changes we personally need to make, then do them and, at the same time, encourage the dynamism and focus within people to make good things happen.

There is not just hope, but real weapons sat waiting for us to pick up and use against climate change and pollution. When this book was first conceived, after a conversation about wooden hangers (yep, really!), it became obvious there were hundreds of thousands of events and things happening, and new products and technologies being developed, to help slow down the damage we are inflicting on the environment. The world just needed to get on board and join in making the change.

The environment could be game-changed and transformed completely if people had a clearer idea of what role they could play - and then got on and did so.

Individuals like you and me. We are the ones who will make the real and effective difference in the fight against climate change - and we could also be the ones who might benefit most from doing so - just by living a more environment minded life. After all, it's not changing people in to something we're not. It's gently taking us back to the kind of people we've been for millions of years. The ones who work with nature not against it - but this time with better information, better tools, and smarter technology.

If climate change is a war, then humanity is presently the equivalent of Britain in the summer of 1940, the Spartans at Thermopylae in 480BC, or the Americans before the Battle of Saratoga in 1777. Losing, but able to create a defining moment that favourably changes the direction of the war.

If we are in a war, maybe you should consider conscripting yourself into the army that want to fight and win that war. Just 2% of your time is one week a year. Just 10% is five weeks. World War Two soldiers fought for six years.

Thank you for reading this book. Good luck making the task you have chosen a success, and please stay in touch to let us know what you are doing at #ChosenToSaveThePlanet

UPSELL MOMENT

It's Time To Do Your Bit! Choose People Who Need to Read This Book - Then Buy Them a Copy

There is a small part of the author both screaming and smiling at this moment with the idea that this serious book now wants to 'upsell' to you - the super wonderful reader. But this is exactly what is happening, and has to happen, if we want to turn our planet around.

Too many good books, filled with good ideas, sit on bookshop shelves because they don't get their message out. With your help, this book is not going to be one of them - it wants to be in the 'action' section' as well as the 'environment' section of the store.

You are now being asked, very politely, to think of as many of your friends, relatives, neighbours, colleagues, employees, employers, even celebs or politicians, that could do with reading this book. Could they too make a difference to the planet?

If the answer is yes (it is!), then buy them this book.

To make it more interesting (and what is the point of life if it isn't interesting?) you could even suggest that if they complete just one task in the book - you will do something for them, or give them something as an incentive.

The 'something' could be 'anything'. You could offer them help in their garden, promise to take them for a meal, give them tickets for the big game or concert, plant a tree in their honour, or just friendly-bribe them with £5, or £10, or some other amount. Be creative. If you were offered a free weekend away, or a bottle of the finest champagne, simply for reading a book and completing one of the tasks, would you be tempted?

If you can, film yourself making the offer/pledge/incentive and post it with the hashtag #ChosenToSaveThePlanet

This book is available from good book stores
or to purchase direct from

ChosenToSaveThePlanet.com